Workbook

Jennifer Heath

Contents

1. How can we eat well? — Page 4
2. Why are some buildings famous? — Page 18
3. How can we protect wild animals? — Page 32
4. What can we do with our trash? — Page 46
5. How can we choose our jobs? — Page 60
6. What happens in extreme conditions? — Page 74
7. How and why do fashions change? — Page 88
8. How has entertainment developed? — Page 102
9. Why are adventure stories popular? — Page 116
10. Why do we raise money for charity? — Page 130
11. How are we similar but different? — Page 144
12. How did people live in the past? — Page 158

1 How can we eat well?

1 What kinds of healthy food do you know? What would you like to learn about healthy food?

....

....

2 Circle the words related to food. What else do you think you will learn about eating well?

    book   butter   drawing   fish   house   vitamins

....

3 BBC 1-1 Watch the video. What snacks do they like? Match the healthy and unhealthy food. Some food words can be used twice.

1 apples
2 fruit
3 oranges
4 bananas
5 melon

a chips
b doughnut
c pizza
d chocolate biscuits
e sour gummy worms
f chocolate cake
g cookies

4 BBC 1-1 Complete the sentences. Watch the video again to check.

    balance   healthier   hungry   fuel   superfoods

1 With the right ...., eating can be one of life's greatest joys.
2 Food is the .... that keeps us going.
3 We're bombarded with choices from sugary drinks and junk food to ....
4 We have to listen to our body so we know when we are .... and when we are not.
5 I know we should eat ...., but I just don't do it sometimes.

Reading 1

1 Look at the pictures and read the first paragraph of *Good Fats*. What's the text about? How do you know?

GOOD FATS

So, eating fat doesn't always make you fat? Yes, that's right. There are good fats and bad fats and we now know which fatty foods are actually good for us! Let's take a look at olive oil and butter – they both contain good fats. Olive oil is great to drizzle on a salad, and it's great to spread butter on a slice of bread. But is one better than the other?

Olive oil and butter help our bodies store energy. Olive oil is a good source of vitamin E and butter is a good source of vitamin D and calcium. But they don't come from the same source. Olive oil is a plant product and butter is a dairy product. Because of this, you shouldn't really eat butter every day. Too much butter can mean weight and heart problems in the future. You can have olive oil every day without these problems.

It's hard to definitely say which is better. The best idea is to eat both, but think about when you use them, so you can count your daily amounts. Don't forget the butter you use to bake biscuits or the oil you use to fry eggs!

2 Read *Good Fats* again. Write **T** (true) or **F** (false).

1 Olive oil contains vitamin E. ....
2 Butter is an animal product. ....
3 A little olive oil can cause heart problems. ....
4 It's healthy to eat two tablespoons of butter every day. ....
5 There's fat in fried eggs. ....

3 Discuss with a friend.

1 What do you spread butter on?
2 How often do you eat salad?
3 What do you like more: olive oil or butter?
4 Can you cook? Do you use olive oil or butter in your cooking?

Vocabulary 1

1 Read and match.

1 A lot of people drizzle
2 Cold butter isn't
3 Cheese is a popular
4 Drink milk for your daily
5 My favorite vegetables
6 Iron is a mineral that

a we can find in our food.
b intake of calcium.
c olive oil on salads.
d are carrots and potatoes.
e easy to spread on bread.
f dairy product.

2 Find and write eight words. What do they have in common?

C	A	R	B	O	H	Y	D	R	A	T	E	S
A	R	K	A	L	F	I	V	R	E	T	V	M
L	O	V	I	T	A	M	I	N	S	I	F	I
C	N	I	B	E	T	V	A	O	I	Q	I	N
I	P	R	O	T	E	I	N	F	I	B	B	N
U	P	O	S	L	I	N	T	A	M	I	E	S
M	I	N	E	R	A	L	S	F	E	A	R	T

1 .... 3 .... 5 .... 7 ....
2 .... 4 .... 6 .... 8 ....

3 Complete with words from Activity 2.

1 We need .... like iron and calcium to be strong.
2 The .... you eat in vegetables helps food move through your body.
3 There's .... in butter and oil.
4 Meat and eggs give us a good intake of ....
5 There are .... in fruit, for example, oranges contain vitamin C.
6 .... give us energy and you can find them in pasta and cereal.

6

4 🎧 01 📋 Listen and draw lines.

Peter   Jim   John

Jane   Anna   Daisy

Vocabulary challenge: tastes

5 Read and add more examples of food to each category.

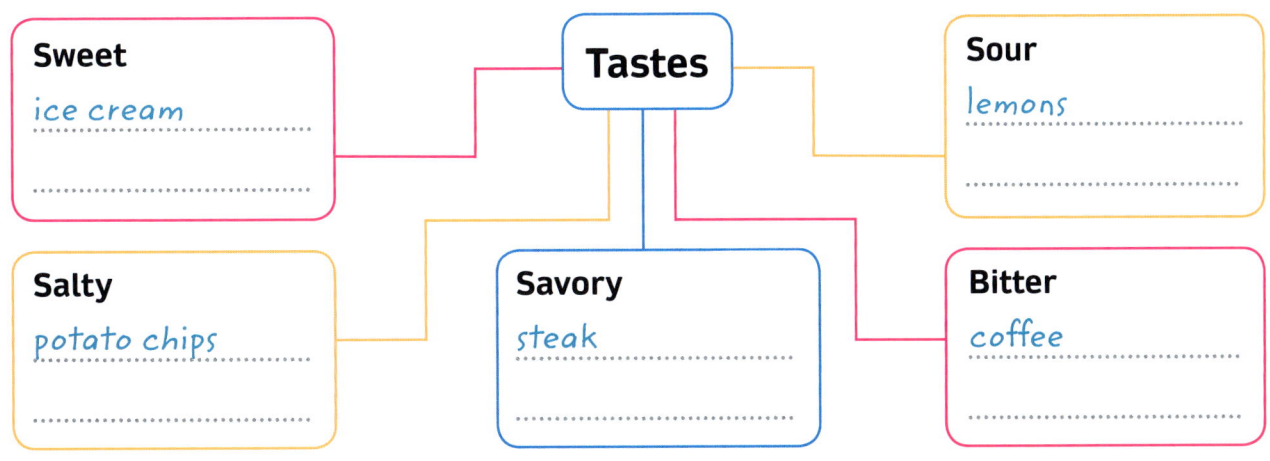

Sweet
ice cream

Tastes

Sour
lemons

Salty
potato chips

Savory
steak

Bitter
coffee

6 Complete the sentences using the tastes.

I don't really like ¹ .... food like ice cream. I prefer ² .... food like cheese and vegetables. But I don't like chips, they're too ³ .... I also don't like dark chocolate, it's ⁴ .... The only dessert I really enjoy is a lime tart. It's quite ⁵ .... because of the juice from limes.

Grammar 1

What are you cooking, Mom? It **smells delicious** and **looks good**.

Wow! Those cakes **look tasty**. Can I try one?

I don't know what this is. It **tastes like** beef, but it **looks like** chicken.

1 Read and circle.

1 What are you cooking? It **smell / smells / smells like** chicken.
2 That soup **look like / looks / looks like** tasty. Can I have a bowl?
3 They say tomatoes are fruit, but they **tastes like / taste like / tastes** vegetables to me.
4 That pizza **look / looks like / looks** good. What's on it?
5 Mom says coffee without sugar **taste like / tastes / tastes like** bitter.
6 Something **smells like / smell like / smells** my favorite pasta! Yummy!

2 Read and match.

1 Is there chocolate in these cookies?
2 Are you making chicken soup?
3 Are these tomatoes from your garden?
4 Is Mom having a hot drink?
5 Is there fruit in this yogurt?
6 What's in these sandwiches?

a The kitchen smells like coffee.
b They look like chocolate chip flavor.
c It tastes like bananas.
d It smells delicious.
e They taste like cheese and tomato.
f They look freshly picked.

3 Look and complete the sentences.

> like   looks   nice   smells   tastes

1 What's the meat in this stew? It looks _____ beef.
2 This meal smells _____ .
3 I love coming to your house. It always _____ like freshly baked cookies.
4 This pancake _____ great. Can I eat it?
5 What's this delicious yellow fruit? It _____ like a tomato.

8

4 Complete with one word in each blank.

Mark: What are you making? It ¹ .... good. Is it a cake?

Sara: No. It smells ² .... a cake, but it's actually a big cookie.

Mark: Does it ³ .... nice?

Sara: I don't know. It's almost ready. Let's see. Does it smell ⁴ .... a cookie or a cake now?

Mark: A cake!

Sara: Oh, no. Well, you can try it.

Mark: Thanks. Yummy! It ⁵ .... delicious. It tastes ⁶ .... a chocolate chip cookie.

Sara: That's because it is a chocolate chip cookie!

5 Write the words in order.

1 tastes / cereal / bananas / like / and / chocolate / this

....

2 pancakes / those / like / hearts / look

....

3 delicious / my / smells / burger

....

4 looks / your / nutritious / breakfast

....

5 chips / taste / cheese / these / like / potato

....

6 Dad / yummy / cookies / is / and / smell / baking / they

....

7 always / yogurt / tastes / fruit / good / with

....

Reading 2

1 Read *Energy Breakfast*. What kind of food is the best for breakfast?

2 Read *Energy Breakfast* again. Stop after each paragraph. Read and circle.

Paragraph 1
1 A nutritious breakfast should always be **sweet and tasty** / **filling and healthy**.

Paragraph 2
2 Hazelnuts and pistachios are **superfoods** / **seeds**.

Paragraph 3
3 A vegetable omelet is **a great superfood breakfast** / **a good idea for lunch**.

Paragraph 4
4 Berries and honey **make us feel tired** / **are great on pancakes**.

Paragraph 5
5 Superfoods are **a taste boost** / **a good breakfast choice**.

3 Think and write.

1 Name a superfood you eat.

2 Which superfood would you like to try?

3 How do you think superfoods make you feel?

ENERGY Breakfast

I need a lot of energy at the start of the day! I do a lot of sports and I realize that I need to eat well to be healthy, so it's important for me to have a nutritious breakfast. It has to be filling and tasty, too. Sometimes I have pancakes with fruit and strawberry jelly. I also like cereal with milk, fruit, and nuts. But my breakfast isn't always sweet. Let's have a closer look at the things I eat.

Superfoods are an important part of my breakfast. They're a great source of energy that lasts all morning. Cereal and milk for breakfast are fine, but I also add superfoods like nuts and seeds to the bowl. They're healthy and also very tasty. I like hazelnuts, pistachio nuts, and pumpkin seeds the best.

Sometimes my mom makes omelets. They're a great idea because eggs have a lot of protein. Maybe it sounds weird for breakfast, but she also adds vegetables for energy when I have sports on the same day. Broccoli is my favorite superfood for omelets.

My favorite breakfast is my mom's pancakes with fruit and jelly. Mom's homemade jelly is made with a superfood – strawberries. In fact, all berries are superfoods. I also drizzle honey on pancakes because it's sweet and tasty.

Do you want an energy boost for breakfast? Then make a sensible choice and eat up your superfoods!

Vocabulary 2

1 Look and match the sentences to the food.

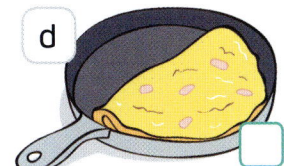

1 This grilled salmon looks tasty.
2 There are two eggs in this omelet.
3 Would you like a boiled egg for breakfast?
4 There's broccoli in my miso soup.
5 Today, I'm having pancakes with jelly.
6 I like noodles with beef.

2 Read and circle.

1 Do you want to spread some butter on your **bread roll / broccoli**?
2 Can I have some miso **jelly / soup** please?
3 This broccoli was **fried / boiled** in salty water.
4 These **pancakes / omelets** with chocolate ice cream are very sweet.
5 Is **beef / salmon** your favorite fish?

3 Complete the sentences with words from Activity 2.

1 Put the _____ egg in an egg cup after you take it out of the hot water.
2 _____ is a tasty meat and it can be served as a steak.
3 To prepare a savory onion _____ you need 4 eggs, milk, butter, and an onion.
4 _____ is my favorite kind of fish.
5 I like _____ chicken with crispy skin. Yum!
6 Green vegetables like _____ have a lot of vitamins and fiber in them.

4 Think and write.

1 What's your favorite breakfast?
....

2 Do you prefer fish or meat? What's your favorite kind?
....

3 What do you like to eat with noodles?
....

4 What's your favorite soup?
....

Word study: synonyms

5 Match the words that have the same meanings.

1 delicious   a weird
2 sugary   b tired
3 sleepy   c healthy
4 strange   d tasty
5 nutritious   e sweet

6 Read and write. Use synonyms from Activity 5.

1 **Jack:** This tea is too sweet.
  Eva: No, it isn't. It isn't .... at all.

2 **Mary:** Are you tired?
  Astrid: Yes, I'm very ....

3 **Diego:** This soup is tasty.
  Ezra: I know. It's ....

4 **Miray:** Is fish a healthy choice?
  Tim: Yes, it's very ....

5 **Irina:** Does this milk taste weird?
  Oli: Yes, it tastes ....

Grammar 2

You can use *will* to talk about quick decisions that you make:

I**'ll look** in the Indian restaurant.

I**'ll eat** more fruit.

I **won't drink** soda every day.

1 Read and match.

1 I'm sorry, I'm busy.
2 Those bags look heavy.
3 Everything looks tasty.
4 Are you hungry?
5 This soup is very salty!
6 I'm not hungry.

a I'll help you!
b I'll just have some juice.
c I'll make you a sandwich.
d I won't eat it.
e I'll take a piece of cherry pie.
f I won't come to your party.

2 Read and complete with *will* or *won't*.

Kyra: Hey Tom, I'm going to the canteen. Would you like anything?

Tom: Actually, I ¹ _____ come with you. I want to see the menu. What ² _____ you have?

Kyra: I don't know. I like italian food, I hope there ³ _____ be pasta. What kind of food do you like?

Tom: Today's Mexican food day, so they ⁴ _____ have pasta. Mexican food is my favorite!

Kyra: Mexican sounds good. And it smells amazing, too. Look! They have quesadillas. I ⁵ _____ take one. How about you?

Tom: I ⁶ _____ have the quesadilla. I think I ⁷ _____ have echiladas. They look delicious!

3 You want to be healthier. What will you do? Write sentences with *will* or *won't*.

1 eat / chocolate ice cream / for breakfast

....

2 have / more vegetables

....

3 put / fruit / in my lunch box

....

4 bake / cookies with Mom / once a week

....

5 have / butter / every day

....

4 Imagine you're at a camp. You have to choose what you'll eat tomorrow. Check the things you prefer. Then write sentences.

breakfast

snack

I will have pancakes for breakfast. I won't

....

lunch

dinner

....

Writing

1 Complete the tips with *should* or *shouldn't*.

MARY'S TIPS!

Eat well, feel well

TIP 1: Eat well in the morning. We ¹............... eat a good breakfast but it ²............... have a lot of sugar in it because sugar doesn't give you enegry for long.

TIP 2: Eat well at lunch time. We ³............... have a very big lunch with a lot of fat because it makes us sleepy. We ⁴............... have a lot of salad and vegetables.

TIP 3: Eat well in the evening. We ⁵............... eat at about 7 o'clock, or at least 3 hours before we go to bed. We ⁶............... eat late so don't have trouble sleeping.

2 Think about your healthy eating tips. Complete the chart with your ideas.

Things we should do	Things we shouldn't do	Healthy foods	What do they contain?

3 Write your tips for healthy eating in your notebook. Use your ideas from Activity 2.

(!) Remember

Check (✓) what your writing has.

a writing strategy: *should* and *shouldn't* to give advice ☐

b vocabulary:
food words ☐
adjectives ☐
verbs ☐

c correct spelling: ☐

15

Now I Know

1 Complete the crossword. What's the hidden word? What does it mean?

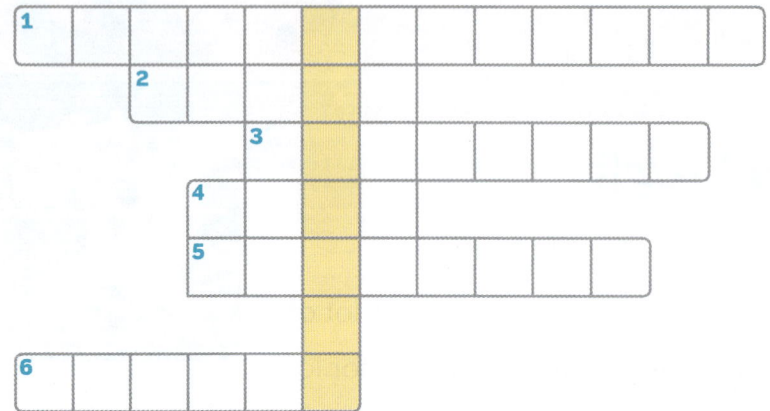

1 Pasta, cereal, and bread have a lot of these.
2 Things cooked in a pan with some fat are …
3 You can make them in a pan and eat them with ice cream or fruit and honey.
4 You drizzle this on your salad.
5 These are in fruits and vegetables, and their names are letters.
6 Milk, yogurt, and butter are this kind of product.

The hidden word is .... It means ....

2 Read, choose, and write.

Health Tips for your Morning!

Start the day with an energy boost. What ¹............ you do that? How about some berries in a bowl of yogurt? You shouldn't add sugar, but a bit of honey ²............ make it sweet, too. Honey ³............ sweet, but it's better for you than sugar. You should also add seeds or nuts to yogurt. They also ⁴............ delicious in cereal or with pancakes. Don't eat sugary things between meals. They may look ⁵............ a delicious snack, but the sugar rush ⁶............ last long!

1	help	will	will help	4	tastes	like	taste
2	will	won't	is	5	likes	like	smells
3	tastes	like	taste	6	won't	will	smell

16

3 Find and circle five words. Then complete the sentences.

calciumgrobreadodainoodlewthgrilledirvegetables

1 I spread a lot of butter on my .... roll.
2 There's .... in all dairy products.
3 My favorite .... are onions and broccoli.
4 Beef .... soup is very tasty and filling.
5 I like .... meat and fish.

4 Circle the odd one out. Then write sentences with the words you circled.

1 salmon   broccoli   beef
2 oil   fiber   butter

3 boiled   bread   cereal
4 pancake   omelet   jelly

....
....
....
....

Things I learn

1 Write down your three favorite new words from this unit. Which word was the most difficult?

....

2 Write two things you found interesting about:

1 eating a balanced diet

2 different kinds of breakfasts

....

3 What good things can you find in food?

....

17

2 Why are some buildings famous?

1 What kinds of buildings do you know? What would you like to learn about buildings?

....
....

2 Circle the words related to architecture. What else do you think you will learn about buildings?

elevator   leaf   legend   roof   stairs   wall

....

3 🎬 2-1 BBC   Watch the video and circle the correct answer.

1 An architect has to understand science, **math / art**, and engineering.
2 Rosie's **mother / sister's husband** told her about architecture.
3 Rosie and Amjad imagine what a building looks like in the **past / future**.
4 They **make a model / do a drawing** of what the power station looks like today.

4 🎬 2-1 BBC   Complete the sentences and match them to the pictures. Watch the video again to check.

> architecture   building site   model   sketches

1 .... help when thinking about the scale and overall look of the pavilion.
2 They saw a gigantic .... of the Battersea Power Station.
3 Alex talked to Rosie and Amjad about why they like ....
4 They visited the .... and talked to someone who's working there.

 a
 b
 c
 d

Reading 1

1 Read *The Eden Project* quickly and answer the questions.

The Eden Project

At the Eden Project in Cornwall, UK, you can see what looks like huge bubbles sitting on the land. These structures are called biomes. Inside the biomes are different plants from all over the world. There's a rainforest biome that is tall enough to fit the Tower of London into it! The Eden Project was designed by Grimshaw Architects and the whole project is bigger than 35 football pitches!

In January 1995, a man called Tim Smit had the idea for the Eden Project. He asked the famous architect Nicholas Grimshaw to design it. They started building it in 1998. It wasn't easy because it rained a lot and the land was not flat. Two years later the biomes were ready and the hard work for the gardeners started. On 17th March, 2001 the Eden Project opened its doors. A million people visited it in the first three months!

In November 2004, they opened an ice rink and in 2008 they finished the education centre called *The Core*. *The Core* has an amazing roof that copies spiral shapes we see in nature. It stays warm because there are recycled newspapers inside the walls. The Eden Project is a great place to visit and learn.

1 Where's the project? ....
2 Who had the idea for the project? ....
3 When did they start to build it? ....
4 What's *The Core*? ....

2 Read *The Eden Project* again and match.

1 The architects of the Eden Project were
2 Nicholas Grimshaw
3 The gardeners started work in
4 On March 17th, 2001
5 In 2004, they opened

a is a famous architect.
b the ice rink.
c the Grimshaw Architects.
d 2000.
e the Eden Project opened.

3 Discuss with a friend. Why do you think places like the Eden Project are so popular?

Vocabulary 1

1 Read and match.

1. The Burj Khalifa is 828
2. The Eden Project attracts
3. The Empire State Building is
4. People use concrete
5. Modern buildings are bigger
6. Biomes are structures

a a massive construction.
b because we started using iron.
c thousands of tourists every day.
d at the Eden Project.
e to build bridges.
f meters tall.

2 Look, read, and complete. Then match.

architect   Bridge   monument   Tower   Statue

1. You can go to the top of the Eiffel _____ in an elevator.
2. The _____ of Liberty is in New York.
3. My dad is an _____. He designs tall buildings.
4. This famous _____ is the Parthenon. It's very old.
5. I saw the Golden Gate _____ when I was in San Francisco.

a

b

c

d

e

3 Find and circle five words in the word snake. Then complete the description.

bridgefgamassiveblometersarkarchitecttmotowercontr

In my town there's a ¹ .... ² .... across the river. It was designed by a very famous ³ .... Thousands of people come to see it every year! It has a crooked ⁴ .... at each end. Each one's 25 ⁵ .... tall.

Word study: antonyms

4 Read and match the opposites.

1 huge — a short
2 tall — b outside
3 old — c tiny
4 hard — d new
5 inside — e easy

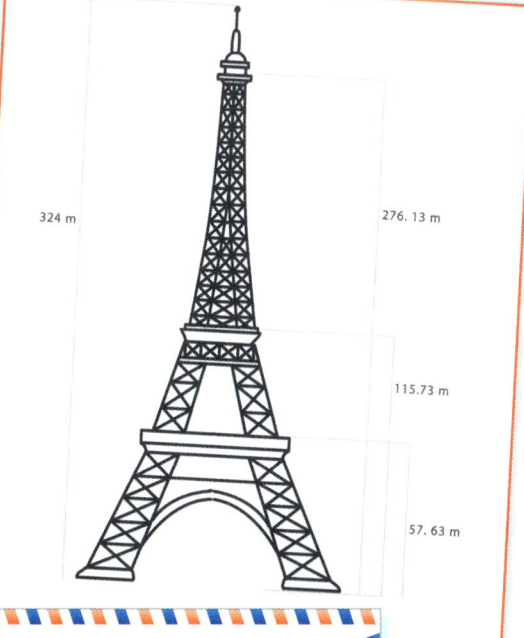

5 Complete with words from Activity 4.

The Eiffel Tower in Paris is very ¹ .... – it's 324 meters high. It's a long way to the top, so it isn't ² .... to climb up. Climbing it is so ³ .... that most people go up in the elevators. The tower stands on four ⁴ .... legs – you feel really ⁵ .... when you stand next to them. The tower is quite ⁶ .... , but the metal often gets ⁷ .... paint so it always looks nice. The architect, Gustave Eiffel, built an apartment for himself at the top. You can take a tour and see what the apartment looks like on the ⁸ ....

Grammar 1

> **How tall** is the Galata Tower?   It's 67 meters **tall**.
> **How long** is the Great Wall of China?   It's 8,000 kilometers **long**.
> **How deep** is the Atlantic Ocean?   It's 8,486 meters **deep**.
> **How far** is Mexico City from New York?   It's 3,360 kilometers **away**.

1 Read and circle.

1 How **long** / **tall** is this bridge? Is it 200 or 300 meters from one side to the other?
2 How **far** / **deep** is the river? Are there fish at the bottom?
3 How **deep** / **tall** is that mountain? Is it more than a kilometer high?
4 How **far** / **long** is London from Paris? Is it more than 100 kilometers?

2 Write questions. Then choose the correct answer.

1 deep / how / the / is / here / ocean
   ....?

2 is / tower / how / tall / that
   ....?

3 the / far / monument / here / from / how / is
   ....?

4 is / street / how / your / long
   ....?

5 tall / over / is / statue / there / how / the
   ....?

6 long / bridge / that / river / over / the / how / is
   ....?

a It's 226 meters tall. ☐
b It's two kilometers away. ☐
c It's a small bridge, only 30 meters long. ☐
d It's about two meters tall. ☐
e It's 2,900 meters deep. ☐
f It's one kilometer long. ☐

22

3   Listen and write.

New York

1. the Empire State Building
   How tall:
2. 5th Avenue
   How long:
3. the Hudson River
   How deep:
4. New York from Washington, D.C.
   How far:

4 Look at the information in Activity 3. Write questions and full answers.

1. Empire State Building
   How tall is the Empire State Building?
   It's 443 meters tall.

2. 5th Avenue

3. the Hudson River

4. New York from Washington, D.C.

Reading 2

1 Read the story. Is Alma excited about her trip to Scotland? How do you know?

A BUSY TRIP!

Adela and Alma spend a lot of time together, both at school and after school. Alma is on the school field hockey team and on the basketball team, and Adela always goes to the games to see her play. Well, almost always. There's a game that she isn't going to see this Saturday. It's the field hockey final.

"Where are you going to go, Alma?"

"We're going to go to Scotland. The other team's from Edinburgh."

"Scotland! That's great! It's going to be cold there in December, so I hope you're going to take some warm clothes."

"Don't worry. I'm not going to get cold on the hockey field. We're all going to run fast and score a lot of goals. But you're right, I'm going to take a warm coat and gloves because we're going to stay an extra day in Edinburgh and have a look around. There are some really cool buildings there. Look, I have a brochure. We're going to visit the castle. I love castles! It's the most important landmark in the city. And we're going to go on an excursion to Arthur's Seat. I can't wait! I'm also going to try a typical Scottish dish. It's called haggis."

Adela looked surprised.

"Are you going to do all that in one day?" she asked.

"Yes, we are. We're going to get up really early and we're going to go to bed really late. And we're going to win the field hockey final too, of course."

2 Read and complete the sentences.

1 We know Adela is happy about Alma's trip because she says _____.
2 We know Alma's going to need warm clothes because _____.
3 We know Alma likes trying new things because _____.
4 We know Adela isn't sure about the extra day because _____.

3 Discuss with a friend. Which landmark in your hometown would you like to show to a foreign visitor? Why?

Vocabulary 2

1 Read and circle.

1 Where's the **brochure** / **mural** about winter vacations?
2 This building is a **medieval** / **typical** example of modern architecture.
3 She's going to go to a sports **belfry** / **camp** for the whole of July.
4 Don't run up the **staircase** / **arches**. You might slip on the stones.
5 The **murals** / **landmarks** on this wall are beautiful.
6 I bet it took a long time to make these **monasteries** / **carved** statues.

2 Complete the crossword.

Across

1 You walk up or down a .... to get to another floor.
4 Something that is usually a certain way is ....
6 A .... is a picture that is painted on a wall.
8 You can read about different places to visit in a ....
9 .... are places where monks live.

Down

2 A lot of of children stay at a summer .... for their vacation.
3 A .... is a building or place that we easily recognize.
5 A postman delivers letters and ....
7 .... are beautiful structures that hold up a building.

3 Look, read, and complete the sentences.

belfry   carved   landmarks   medieval   staircase

In France, there are a lot of ⁱ .... castles to visit. These castles are important ² .... in their areas and great to explore. A lot of castles have fun activities for kids so they're a great day out for the family.

Inside this castle you can go up a narrow ³ .... that is ⁴ .... in stone. There are great views from the ⁵ .... at the top of the tower.

Vocabulary challenge: parts of a house

4 Look and label the diagram.

chimney   driveway   gutter   porch   shutter

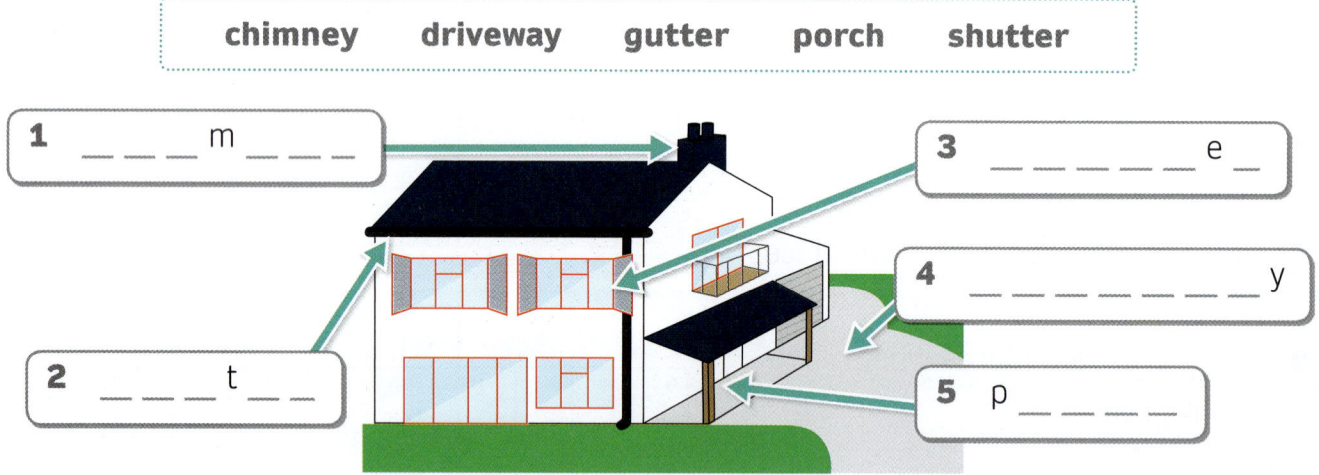

1 _ _ _ m _ _ _
2 _ _ _ _ t _ _
3 _ _ _ _ _ _ e _
4 _ _ _ _ _ _ _ y
5 p _ _ _ _

5 Complete with the words from Activity 4.

1 You can't leave your car here! The sign says "Don't park in the ...."
2 Let's sit outside on the .... and enjoy the warm day.
3 This house has a .... so we can have a real fire in the living room.
4 A storm's coming! Make sure to close the .... !
5 Can you clean the .... ? I think it's been blocked by leaves.

Grammar 2

I**'m going to do** a lot of different activities.

You**'re going to travel** to Australia **next year**.

Rachel **isn't going to spend** the whole day studying.

My parents **are going to travel** to Spain for vacation **next** summer.

Are you **going to study** all day? No, I**'m not**.

Going to + verb refers to decisions taken before the time of speaking.

1 Underline *be going to* and circle the word that follows it. Then match.

1 Dave's going to see the Eiffel Tower.
2 We're going to swim in the ocean.
3 I'm going to go to summer camp.
4 Mom's going to drive on our vacation.
5 They're going to read brochures later.
6 You're going to travel by train.

27

2 Complete the sentences with the information in the chart and *going to/not going to*.

Sara's vacation plans	My vacation plans	Mark and Mary's vacation plans
visit Pisa	stay in Istanbul	travel to New York
go to the Leaning Tower	see the Galata Tower	explore the Guggenheim museum
go by train	go by plane	go by plane

1 Sara .... of Pisa. She .... New York.
2 Mark and Mary .... the Galata Tower. They .... the Guggenheim museum.
3 I .... Istanbul. I .... of Pisa.
4 Mary, Mark, and I .... by plane. Sara .... by train.

3 What are they going to do? Write and answer the questions.

1 Kelly / go on / summer camp

.... ?

✗ ....

2 your parents / fly to / the U.S.A.

.... ?

✓ ....

3 you and Jim / visit / a museum

.... ?

✓ ....

4 your vacation / be / boring

.... ?

✗ ....

4 Complete the questions. Then answer for you.

1 Are you going .... study all day today?
2 .... your friend going to visit you tomorrow? ....
3 What are you .... to do this weekend? ....

28

Writing

1 Read, underline the names, and circle the numbers.

Graceland

Graceland is a popular tourist attraction in Memphis. It was the home of the famous singer Elvis Presley. A man called Stephen Toof owned the land and he named it after his daughter Grace. Grace's niece built the house in 1939 and she asked architects at the company Furbringer and Ehrmanis to design this beautiful mansion. Elvis Presley bought Graceland in 1957 and he lived there with his family and parents. The house has eight bedrooms, a music room, and a TV room. Today the house is a museum.

2 Find information about the famous house you chose. Write down the facts, numbers, and names.

Name: ....
Location: ....
Owner/Architect: ....
Important dates: ....

3 Write your description of a building in your notebook. Use your ideas from Activity 2.

⚠ Remember

Check (✓) what your writing has.

a writing strategy:
   numbers ☐
   names ☐
   facts ☐

b vocabulary:
   architecture words ☐
   buildings ☐

c correct spelling: ☐

Now I Know

1 Read and circle.

1 Let's climb to the top of this **mural** / **package** / **tower** to see the view of the city.
2 I'm going to choose a vacation from this **brochure** / **construction** / **statue** about Turkey.
3 We visited the Statue of Liberty. It's a famous **belfry** / **staircase** / **monument** in New York.
4 This old building has unusual **carved** / **typical** / **concrete** stonework.
5 The **arches** / **construction** / **structure** of a tall building can take many months.

2 Read and write the words.

> architect   attract   bridge   camp   concrete
> landmark   medieval   meters   monastery   typical

1 A word that describes a time period about 800 years ago. ....
2 This person designs buildings. ....
3 You use them to measure length. ....
4 This is a famous structure everybody knows. ....
5 You use this material to build with. ....
6 This is a monk's home. ....

3 Complete the words.

1 Famous landmarks a_ _ _ _ _ _ thousands of tourists each year.
2 Most kids love going to a summer c_ _ _ in the summer.
3 A m_ _ _ _ can make a regular wall look beautiful.
4 Tokyo is well-known for its m_ _ _ _ _ _ buildings with a lot of floors.
5 A b_ _ _ _ _ _ is the top of a tower where the bell is.
6 An a_ _ _ _ is a s_ _ _ _ _ _ _ _ _ that supports the weight of a building.

30

4 Read and complete.

Hi Andre,

I'm ¹ .... to look at websites for excursions this evening. ² .... you going to come to my house to help? It's just you and me because Sandra ³ .... going to come with us. She's going ⁴ .... visit her grandma on Saturday instead. Dad asked me, "Are we going to go by train?" and I said, "No, we ⁵ ....!" because my ⁶ .... to take us in his car.

See you later!
Terry

5 Complete the questions. Then answer for you.

1 .... is the tallest building in your hometown?

....

2 .... is the street you live on?

....

Things I learn

1 Write down your three favorite new words from this unit. Which word was the most difficult?

....

2 Write two things you found interesting about:

1 famous buildings   2 constructing buildings

....

....

3 Which landmark in the world would you like to visit?

....

3 How can we protect wild animals?

1 What animals shouldn't be kept as pets? What else would you like to learn about animals?

....

....

2 Circle the words related to wild animals. What do you think you will learn about them?

      car   computer   forest   leaves   shell   snake

....

3 Watch the video and circle the correct answer.

1 There are only about **seven hundred** / **five hundred** mountain gorillas left in the wild.
2 The number of gorillas in the wild will **rise** / **fall**.
3 **Rhinos** / **Gorillas** can weigh over two tones.
4 Rhino horns can cost **sixteen** / **sixty** thousand US dollars per kilo.
5 Today, there are over **seventeen** / **seven** thousand white rhinos in Africa.

4 Read the sentences from the video. Match the highlighted words to their definitions.

1 It's all due to the hard work of those who have chosen to protect this **magnificent** animal.
2 It feels quite **vulnerable** to be so close.
3 The guide makes me **stand my ground** as he comes in for a closer look.
4 We try and keep a respectful distance, so we don't **disturb** the gorillas as they feed.
5 It can actually **fetch** as much as 60,000 US dollars per kilo.

a be sold for a particular amount of money
b stay where you are when someone threatens you
c easy to attack or hurt
d to make someone feel worried or upset
e very impressive and beautiful

32

Reading 1

1 Read *Save Our Animals!*. Then check (✓) the opinions the author expresses in the article.

Save Our Animals!

Last month I watched a documentary about amazing animals on TV. I loved learning new things about tuna, gorillas, leopards, and turtles. Sadly, many of them are now endangered and need our help. I think it's important to learn more about the endangered species and to teach everyone about the wonderful wildlife, birds, fish, and plants that live close to you. How?

Here are some ideas:

You can go to a local animal rescue center and ask about how you can help – rescue centers often need volunteers.

You can ask a teacher at school to help you find out what species of animals and plants are in your country. You can make a list of them to see which ones are endangered and find out how to protect them.

You can write a school magazine about wildlife in your area. This is a good idea to help young people learn about the wildlife close to them and how to protect it. You can show the magazine to everyone in your neighborhood.

You can ask your parents' permission to start a wildlife blog. You can take pictures of the animals' habitats and the problems you find there, like trash, then post the pictures on the blog and organize a clean-up of the local environment.

1. We can't teach people about wildlife. ☐
2. Helping at rescue centers is a good idea. ☐
3. A school magazine won't help young people learn. ☐
4. You should ask your parents before starting a blog. ☐

2 What ways of helping animals does the author propose?

1 .... 3 ....
2 .... 4 ....

3 Work with a friend. Think and circle the things you can do. You can add your own ideas.

I can help clean up a habitat.   I can write for a school magazine.

33

Vocabulary 1

1 Read and match.

1 The leatherback
2 Animals are protected at a national
3 Mountain
4 A snow
5 Bluefin
6 The rainforest

a gorillas are vegetarian.
b is home to a lot of birds.
c leopard lives high up in the mountains.
d tuna is endangered.
e turtle eats plastic by mistake.
f park.

2 Read and complete the words.

Animals Under Threat

When a species is [1] d _ _ _ _ _ _ ed, they're declared extinct by the International Union for Conservation of Nature (IUCN). A lot of [2] s _ e _ _ _ _ of animals are [3] e _ _ _ _ _ _ _ d and that means they might all [4] _ _ _ a _ _ _ _ _ soon. One reason for this is that animals hunt other animals.

[5] P _ a _ _ _ _ _ are another danger. They hunt animals without permission. They kill rhinos for their horns, elephants for their tusks, and tigers for their fur. Park rangers do their best to [6] p _ _ _ _ _ _ _ them from killing animals.

3 Read and complete the sentences.

destroyed   disappeared   endangered   prevent   species

1 There are a lot of different _____ of fish in the ocean. Tuna is one of them.
2 We can _____ sealife from dying by not dropping plastic bags in the ocean.
3 Many animal species have already _____ because people _____ their habitat.
4 A lot of animals are _____ so they need protection to survive.

4   Think and write.

1 What species of animals live in rainforests?

....

....

Vocabulary challenge: animal habitats

5 Decode the words. Then match them to the pictures.

A	B	C	D	E	F	G	H	I	J	K	L	M	N	O	P	Q	R	S	T	U	V	W	X	Y	Z
1	2	3	4	5	6	7	8	9	10	11	12	13	14	15	16	17	18	19	20	21	22	23	24	25	26

1

__ __ __ __ __ __
23 5 20 12 1 14 4

__ __ __ __ __ __ __ __ __
7 18 1 19 19 12 1 14 4

4

2

__ __ __ __ __ __
20 21 14 4 18 1

5

__ __ __ __ __ __ __ __
23 15 15 4 12 1 14 4

3

__ __ __ __ __
3 15 1 19 20

6

__ __ __ __ __
1 18 3 20 9 3

6 Write each animal's habitat. Use the words from Activity 5.

1 penguin - ....
2 alligator - ....
3 seagull - ....

4 sheep - ....
5 squirrel - ....
6 reindeer - ....

35

Grammar 1

> **How many** animals were there in the cage?
> **How much** money is he going to make?
>
> We use *How many* with **countable** nouns.
> We use *How much* with **uncountable** nouns.

1 Circle the countable nouns. Underline the uncountable nouns.

1 How many pictures did you take?
2 How much bread do we have?
3 How many different pets does she have?
4 How much milk did we drink?
5 How much food are we going to need?
6 How many eggs do you want?

2 Write the words in order. Then match the questions to the correct answers.

1 you / much / did / water / yesterday / how / drink

....?

2 do / have / how / pets / you / many

....?

3 bag / bananas / there / how / are / many / in / the

....?

4 eat / do / much / elephants / food / how

....?

a There are five bananas in the bag. ☐
b Elephants eat a lot of food. ☐
c I have one pet. ☐
d I drank a lot of water. ☐

3 Complete the questions. Then look at the picture and write the answers.

1 .... backpacks are there? ....
2 .... gorillas are there? ....
3 .... water is there? ....
4 .... men are there? ....
5 .... birds are there? ....
6 .... food do the gorillas have? ....

4 Read the answers and write questions.

1 *How much water is there in the ocean?*
There's a lot of water in the ocean.

2 ....?
There are about 700 gorillas in the rainforest.

3 ....?
Lions sleep many hours every day.

4 ....?
National parks need a lot of money.

5 ....?
There are twenty tigers at this national park.

Reading 2

1 Read *Polar Bear*. What's the message of the poem?

Polar Bear

Dangerous, white
Arctic, cold.
I walk on ice
What a cold life.
I'm happy alone.
But it's too warm.
Slowly. Melting. My home.
Is it only me?
How many animals
Want to live free?
Our habitats disappear
Hunters kill
Builders build.
We run in fear
And I feel
We're all lost.

The tuna are
Beautiful, rainbow blue.
They swim
In deep oceans.
They swim in waves
But the water is polluted.
They swim into nets
So now they're on
The endangered list.
Hear the story
Of the black rhino
And listen. Think.
"Don't look for me,"
He says.
"I can't pose for photos
You won't find me.
Not because I'm shy.
No, that's not it.
I was big and fast.
Was. Not now."
Extinct. Another list.

Our stories are sad
I wish we had
A way to prevent
The hunting
The poaching
The polluting
The building.
Can you help?
All we want
Is our home.

2 Read *Polar Bear* again and write the name of an animal.

1 This animal lives in a cold place that is getting warmer.
2 This animal is on a list of extinct species.
3 They swim in dirty water.
4 Fishing nets are a danger for these animals.

3 Discuss with a friend. Can you see any of the animals from the poem in your local zoo? Are zoos a good way of protecting animals?

Vocabulary 2

1 Find and circle eight words. Then sort.

W	H	I	S	P	E	R	G
H	S	U	R	V	I	O	P
G	U	S	C	O	R	A	L
L	R	K	O	A	L	M	A
I	V	B	A	M	B	O	O
D	I	T	T	R	A	C	G
E	V	U	H	O	M	O	L
H	E	C	T	A	R	E	I

Verbs
1 ....
2 ....
3 ....
4 ....

Nouns
5 ....
6 ....
7 ....
8 ....

2 Complete the sentences with the words from Activity 1.

1 A lot of species of sealife live in the .... in the ocean.
2 Let me .... this in your ear. Don't tell anyone.
3 One .... of this forest was destroyed today.
4 Pandas eat kilos of .... every day.
5 Some species won't .... without our help.
6 Our pet cat can leave the house and is free to .... the backyard.
7 We couldn't see the lion on the savannah because its yellow .... helped it hide.
8 We watched the fish .... under the waves.

39

3 Write the letters in order. Then choose three words and write sentences.

1 s l e l h ....
2 e d p r o r a t ....
3 r v s i v u e ....
4 o l p r a   r e a b ....
5 i s r p e w h ....
6 s k s u t ....

....
....
....

Word study: synonyms

4 From each line, cross out the word that is not a synonym.

1	extinct	dead	endangered	gone
2	habitat	species	home	territory
3	roam	walk	shout	wander
4	prevent	stop	block	whisper
5	protected area	national park	predator	nature reserve
6	hectare	coat	fur	hair

5 Read and write. Use synonyms from Activity 4.

1 Lions usually have light brown fur. The .... of a tiger is orange and black.
2 Yellowstone Park in the United States is protected area. It's my favorite ....
3 The dodo was a bird, but it's extinct now. It's .... and you cannot see it anymore.
4 Patrols can stop poachers. We have to .... them from killing animals.
5 This park is the .... of many species of birds. It's their home and they return here every year.
6 Big cats .... around their territory to protect it. They can walk up to 50 kilometers in a day!

40

Grammar 2

Look! I **can** run very fast!
Could you ride a bike when you were five?
I **couldn't** run fast when I was very young.

1 Read and circle.

Marco: Grandpa, ¹ **can** / **could** you watch TV when you were young?
Grandpa: No, I ² **couldn't** / **could**. We didn't have a TV.
Marco: So, what did you do for fun?
Grandpa: Well, our street was quiet, so we ³ **could** / **couldn't** play soccer outside.
Marco: That sounds great! I ⁴ **can't** / **can** do that today. There are a lot of cars.
Grandpa: ⁵ **Couldn't** / **Can** you go to the backyard?
Marco: Yes, I ⁶ **can** / **can't**. But it's small so I ⁷ **can't** / **couldn't** run around.
Grandpa: Let's go to the park then! I ⁸ **could** / **can** come with you.
Marco: OK! Thanks, Grandpa, you're the best!

2 What could or couldn't they do? Look at the pictures and write.

1 Dave _____ emails when he was ten.
2 My parents _____ tennis when they were young.
3 Helen _____ a bike when she was six.
4 Jayden _____ German when he was four.

3 Read the text. Choose and complete.

My Grandma's Cat

My Grandma got a pet kitten twelve years ago. Her kitten ¹ _____ climb trees, but it ² _____ come down on its own! This was a big problem, because Grandma ³ _____ reach her kitten at the top of the tree. Grandma wasn't very old then, but she ⁴ _____ climb a tree safely. Luckily, my dad was pretty good at climbing trees. Today, Grandma's cat is very old and lazy. It ⁵ _____ climb trees anymore!

1 can   could   couldn't
2 could   couldn't   can't
3 couldn't   could   can't
4 could   couldn't   can't
5 can't   could   couldn't

4 Complete the questions. Answer for you.

1 _____ you spell well when you were four? ....

2 _____ your mom play the piano when she was young? ....

3 _____ any of your classmates speak German? ....

4 _____ your dad play soccer now? ....

42

Writing

1 Read and complete the text with *so* or a cross (✗).

Let's Clean the Oceans!

Home · Blog · About · Contact

We're Sealife Protection .... and we think that sealife habitats are in danger. We try to think of different ways to help. We care about turtles, jellyfish, and coral, ... we started this group to help them. We believe they need to have clean water and not polluted habitats, ... we try to convince people .... not to drop plastic bags and trash in the oceans.

2 Read and match.

1 Turtles can accidentally eat plastic — a so you can't see it anymore in the wild.
2 Lions are wild animals — b so we should find a way to clean the oceans.
3 The West African black rhino is extinct — c so they shouldn't live in people's homes.

3 Think about the animal you chose. Plan your writing.

1 Name of the animal: ....
2 Habitat: ....
3 Why it's endangered: ....
4 How we can help it: ....
5 What we should teach people: ....

4 Write about your animal in your notebook. Use your ideas from Activity 3.

(!) Remember

Check (✓) what your writing has.

a writing strategy:
   so ☐

b vocabulary:
   habitat ☐
   animals ☐

c correct spelling: ☐

43

Now I Know

1 Find eight words in the word snake. Complete the phrases with some of the words.

bearpoacoatrvleopardheparkgrshellrispecieswitunapeturtle

1 endangered ....
2 snow ....
3 bluefin ....
4 leatherback ....
5 polar ....
6 national ....

2 Read and circle.

1 The **poacher / predator** killed the rhino to sell its horn.
2 The **coral / tusks** on the elephant are its teeth.
3 Animals should be free to **roam / prevent** in their territory.
4 Only about six or seven hundred gorillas live in their natural **habitat / hectare**.
5 Some animals need **national park / hectares** of forest to survive.
6 Pandas can survive on just **rainforest / bamboo**.
7 Fish **whisper / glide** in the water in a beautiful way.
8 We will never see species that are **endangered / destroyed**. They're gone forever.

3 Read and complete.

| can | can | can | can you | could | could you | couldn't | couldn't |

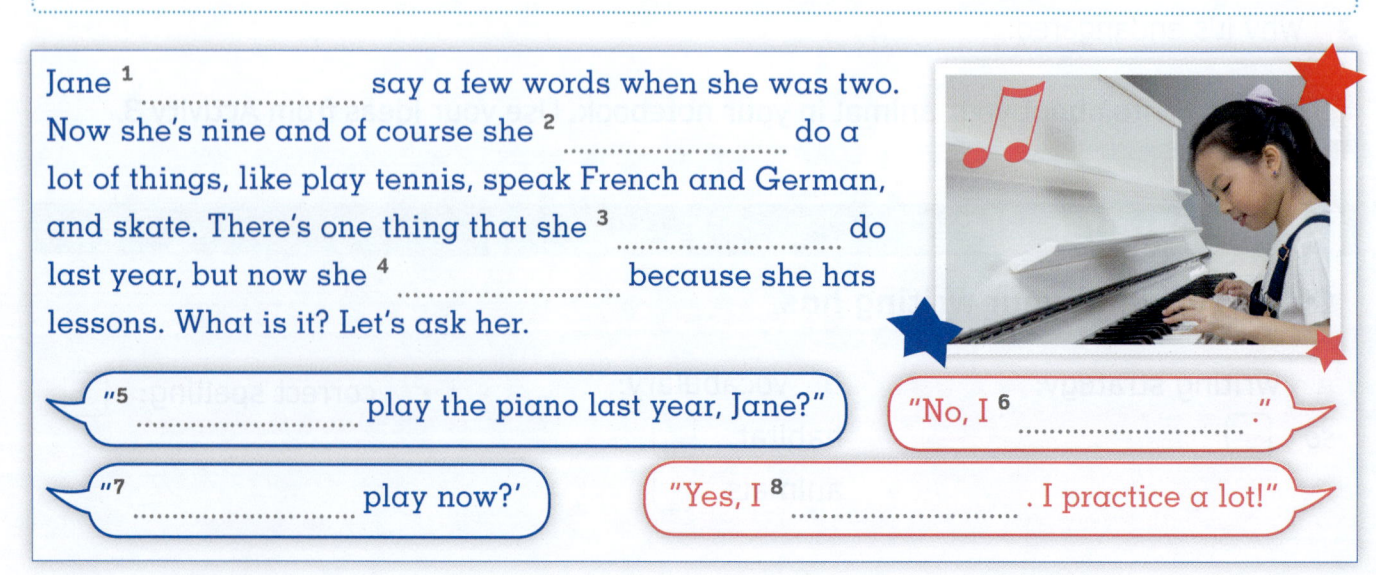

Jane [1] .... say a few words when she was two. Now she's nine and of course she [2] .... do a lot of things, like play tennis, speak French and German, and skate. There's one thing that she [3] .... do last year, but now she [4] .... because she has lessons. What is it? Let's ask her.

"[5] .... play the piano last year, Jane?"

"No, I [6] ...."

"[7] .... play now?"

"Yes, I [8] .... I practice a lot!"

4 Complete the questions with *much* or *many*. Then match and answer.

1 How .... toads are there?

2 How .... bamboo do you feed it?

3 How .... fish were in the tank?

4 How .... bread is there?

5 How .... water do we have?

6 How .... bananas do you need?

a b c d e f

Things I learn

1 Write down your three favorite new words from this unit. Which word was the most difficult?

....

2 Write two things you found interesting about:

1 animal habitats

....

....

2 helping endangered animals

....

....

3 Why do animals become extinct?

....

4 What can we do with our trash?

1 Do you know how to segregate trash? What would you like to learn about it?

....

....

2 Circle the words related to trash. What else do you think you will learn about dealing with trash?

bottle   extinct   flower   plastic   tiger   trash can   waste

....

3 🎬 BBC 4-1 Watch the video and answer the questions.

1. What shapes of foam does Michelle use to cover the umbrella? ....
2. How many segments are on the umbrella? ....
3. Is the foam easy to cut? ....
4. Where can you buy the bright blue foam? ....
5. What are the pink circles for? ....
6. What number does Michelle use for the pupils of the eyes? ....

4 🎬 BBC 4-1 Read and complete. Watch the video again to check.

| cuts   draws   folds   pop   sticks |

1. She .... the shapes with a black marker pen.
2. Michelle .... out the shapes with scissors.
3. The suckers .... out from the white tentacles.
4. Michelle .... one side of the circle over the other to create a cone shape.
5. She .... the last tentacle on with glue.

Reading 1

1 Read *Throwing Out Plastic*. Then check (✓) the sentences that are true for you.

Throwing Out Plastic

Recycling is an excellent way to save energy and take care of the environment. Many countries in Europe recycle more than 50% of their waste, but hundreds of millions of tons of plastic and other waste are still sent to landfills.

We all know that we should recycle plastic, but what happens to it when we just throw it out?

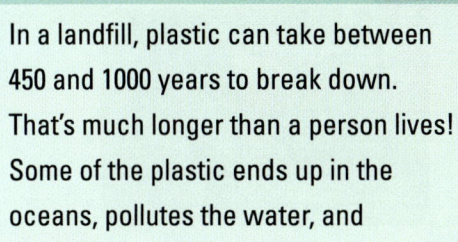

In a landfill, plastic can take between 450 and 1000 years to break down. That's much longer than a person lives! Some of the plastic ends up in the oceans, pollutes the water, and endangers sealife.

So why do we use and then throw out plastic? Well, it's partly because we use it for food and drinks. When we finish what we're eating or drinking, we just throw the packaging away.

Another problem is plastic shopping bags. We all get a plastic bag when we go shopping. We don't usually reuse it.

In fact, we use a plastic bag for an average of 12 minutes. What's more, we only recycle about one bag for every seven bags we use, which means that thousands of shopping bags end up in trash.

So next time you want to throw out something plastic, think about it first.

- I use plastic bags when I go shopping. ☐
- I buy drinks in plastic bottles. ☐
- I reuse plastic bags. ☐
- I throw away empty plastic bottles. ☐

2 Read *Throwing Out Plastic* again and match.

1. We should
2. Plastic ends up in landfills
3. We use plastic for
4. We don't use bags for

a. food and drinks.
b. recycle plastic.
c. a long time.
d. and the oceans.

3 Discuss with a friend. What can you Reduce, Reuse, and Recycle? Use the phrases from the box. Can you add one more idea to each of the three Rs?

> clothes   food packaging   shoes   shopping bags   water bottles

Vocabulary 1

1 Find and circle six words. Then look and write.

dlqo**plastic**jpl**metal**qworeg**fumes**avnldi**cans**lpa**soil**kilwm**fleece**ws

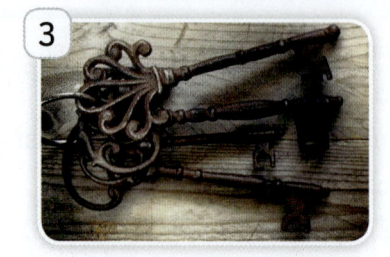

1 ....
2 ....
3 ....
4 ....
5 ....
6 ....

2 Read and circle.

1 You need more **soil** / **metal** / **can** in the pot for your plant.
2 The sun's energy is a **glass** / **natural** / **toxic** resource.
3 Is this bottle made of **packaging** / **process** / **plastic**?
4 The trash you throw out goes to the **fumes** / **landfill** / **fleece**.

3 Read and complete the missing letters. Then match.

1 I can't breathe in this pollution.   a It's made from f __ e __ __ __ .
2 I love my new jacket.   b It's a n __ t __ __ l r __ s __ __ __ __ __ .
3 Do you have any jelly?   c The air is t __ x __ c.
4 The sun gives us energy.   d You should segregate food p __ ck __ ging.
5 Put the cereal box in the paper bin. e It's a new pr __ __ c __ __ __ __ .
6 We now use recycled plastic.   f Yes, it's in that gl __ ss j __ r in the fridge.

48

4 Think about things you buy often. What kind of packaging do they have? Is it good for the environment?

....

Vocabulary challenge: natural resources

5 Read and label the pictures with the words in bold.

1 You can see red **sandstone** at the Lower Antelope Canyon in Arizona.
2 I make pots, cups, and vases with **clay**.
3 Do you know how much **lumber** you can get from a tree?
4 Is this statue made of **marble**? It's so smooth!
5 Silver is found in nature as **ore**. You have to process it to make it into other things.

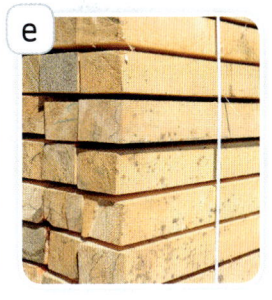

a .... b .... c .... d .... e ....

6 Complete the dialog. Use the words from Activity 5.

1 **Yunny:** Why do you need so much ....?
   Matt: Oh, I'm making a new table and a bench.
2 **Elif:** Did you buy this vase?
   Aisha: No. I made it myself from ....
3 **Pedro:** Is .... easy to work with?
   Sonia: Yes! That's why many sculptors use it to make their statues.
4 **Ella:** Hey, look at this rock! Why is it so shiny?
   Phil: Wow! I think it's a gold and silver ....
5 **Maria:** I like your kitchen floor. Why is it so red?
   Petra: Thanks! It's because the tiles are made of ....

49

Grammar 1

> More people **need to** recycle more at home.
> You **don't need to** have a lot of money to start a Three Rs project at school.
> **Do** we **need to** use so much paper? No, we **don't**.

1 Write sentences. Use the correct form of *need to*.

1 ✓ people / save water
   People need to save water.

2 ✗ I / buy new shoes
   ....

3 ✓ you / use less plastic
   ....

4 ✗ you / wear a sweater
   ....

2 Read Grace's list. Complete the dialog.

Weekend jobs	
✓ recycle the soda cans	✗ wash the soda cans
✓ wash glass jars	✗ cook dinner

Alex: Hi, Grace. Can I help you with your jobs?

Grace: Sure. Can you grab the soda cans?

Alex: Do we ¹............................ them?

Grace: Yes, ²............................ .

Alex: Do we ³............................ the cans, too?

Grace: No, ⁴............................ . But we ⁵............................ the glass jars. There's still some jelly in them.

Alex: OK. I can do that. Do I ⁶............................ dinner?

Grace: No, ⁷............................ . I'm going to order pizza.

3 Write one thing you need to do and one thing you don't need to do today.

1 ....

2 ....

We **could make** a recycling plan for the school. What do you think?

Good idea! We **could reuse** last year's pencils.

Could we **ask** the older students to help us?

We use **could** to make suggestions and to talk about possible actions. We never put the word *to* after **could**.

4 Look and complete. Use *could* and the verbs from the box. Then match.

| ask | make | recycle | reuse |

Vicky and Bob's plan

1 We .... plastic bottles for plants.
2 We .... a drawing for the fridge.
3 We .... our mom to help.
4 We .... our old comic books.

5 Write the words in order.

1 ask / to / I / cousin / could / us / help / my

....

2 box / for / we / could / this / reuse / something

....?

3 these / metal / we / cans / could / recycle

....

6 Write four things you could do to help the environment.

1 ....
2 ....
3 ....
4 ....

Reading 2

1 Read *Dad's New Idea*. Stop at the sentence in bold. Which kitchen items do you think they used to make the gift?

Dad's New Idea

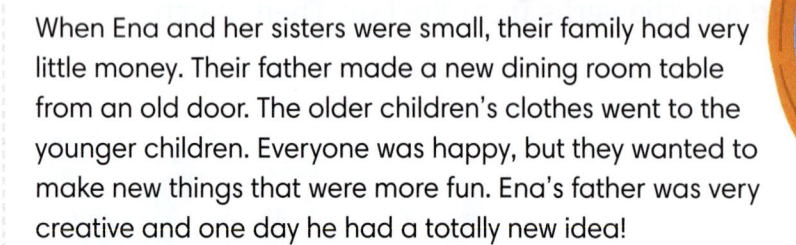

When Ena and her sisters were small, their family had very little money. Their father made a new dining room table from an old door. The older children's clothes went to the younger children. Everyone was happy, but they wanted to make new things that were more fun. Ena's father was very creative and one day he had a totally new idea!

They never bought birthday presents. But Ena's dad told his daughters his idea.

"Tomorrow's Mum's birthday and we're going to make presents with things we find in the kitchen and the garden. Mum's out, so we can make the presents now."

Ena and her sisters loved their father's idea. **They all ran to the kitchen.**

Ena found a bag of pasta that was three different colours. Ena's father found some colourful string. Ena tried a few things and in the end she decided to make a pretty necklace.

Ena's sisters found an empty plastic bottle. They decorated the bottle with modelling clay and beads. Then they picked flowers from the garden and put them in the vase.

The next day, the girls gave their presents to their mother. "Happy Birthday, Mum!" they sang. Mum was very happy. She wore her pretty pasta necklace, she smelt the pretty flowers and put them and the bottle vase in the living room. "Thank you, girls!" she said and gave them all a kiss.

2 Read *Dad's New Idea* again and circle.

1 Ena's father was **happy** / **sad** / **creative**.
2 The gifts were for Ena's **father** / **sisters** / **mother**.
3 Ena used some **eggs** / **pasta** / **flower** for her gift.
4 Ena's sisters upcycled a used plastic **pasta** / **string** / **bottle**.
5 The gifts were **wild** / **pretty** / **three-colored**.

3 Discuss with a friend. Have you ever upcycled anything? Would you be happy to get an upcycled gift?

Vocabulary 2

1 Read and circle.

1 Let's **upcycle** / **create** this bottle and make it into a flower pot.
2 Mom likes her coffee in this big **tire** / **cup**.
3 Anything you put in the recycling bin goes to the **stuff** / **recycling plant**.

2 Read and complete.

> cardboard   decorations   create   picture frame
> recycling plant   throw out   tires   toilet paper rolls   wood

My name's Jack. I visited my friend yesterday and he showed me a ¹_____ his grandma decorated with old string and shells she found at the beach. It was so cool! She agreed to teach us some crafts, too!

It was a fun afternoon. She showed us how to make different party ²_____ from old things. She had a few ³_____ that she didn't ⁴_____ from her bathroom. They're made of ⁵_____, so they're easy to cut and paint. We made colorful napkin rings from them.

We also ⁶_____ some party hats. We used cereal bowls as a template to cut out circles out of old paper. Then we made them into cone shapes, painted, and decorated them. I'll make some more for my birthday party next month!

3 Choose the best name for the story and check (✓).

Jack's party ☐
Making party decorations ☐
Jack's grandma ☐

4 Circle the odd one out. Then write sentences with the words you circled.

1 picture frames   tire   decorations
2 throw out   create   wood
3 stuff   cardboard   wood

....
....
....

Word study: phrasal verbs with *out*

5 Match the phrasal verbs to their meanings.

1 throw out   a cut a shape from a piece of paper

2 eat out   b give something to each person in a group

3 cut out   c get rid of something that you don't want or need

4 hand out   d be very easy to see or notice

5 stand out   e eat in a restaurant instead of at home

6 Read and complete. Use the phrasal verbs from Activity 5.

1 Evan likes wearing bright clothes. They make him .... in the crowd.
2 To make the card, first .... the heart shape, then decorate it.
3 Olive, could you .... the books, please? There's one for everyone.
4 We don't .... often. We prefer eating at home.
5 Don't .... that pretty bottle. You can use it as a vase.

Grammar 2

There's **too much** waste in the trash can.

There are **too many** things in my bag.

We don't have **enough** money to buy that book!

Are there **enough** boxes to collect everything?

1 Read and circle. Then match.

1 I have too **many** / **much** books. I can't read them all.
2 There's too **many** / **much** trash in the bin. I can't throw out more.
3 We have too **much** / **many** clothes. We need to give some away.
4 There's too **much** / **many** candy in the glass jar. I can't close it.

a   b   c   d

2 Read and complete. Use *too much*, *too many*, or *enough*.

1 Do we have _____ cheese to make quesadillas for everyone?
2 I put _____ eggs in this omelet. I can't eat it all.
3 This winter there's _____ snow. Grandpa can't go out.
4 There were _____ people on the bus. I couldn't get in!
5 Sorry. I put _____ salt in the sauce. It's very salty.
6 There's _____ butter on this toast. I don't like it.
7 There isn't _____ time to finish this activity! The lesson's about to end.

3 Write the words in order.

1 time / supper / to / I / don't / cook / enough / have
   ....

2 put / much / tea / I / in / too / sugar / my
   ....

3 money / gifts / enough / Juan / have / for / doesn't
   ....

4 too / family / out / many / my / bottles / throws / plastic
   ....

5 here / much / there's / noise / too / in
   ....

6 for / do / have / information / you / your / enough / project
   .... ?

4 Read, circle, and write for you. Use *enough* or *too much/many*. Then write two of your own ideas.

1 There **are** / **aren't** .... people in my town.
2 There **is** / **isn't** .... noise in my town.
3 I **have** / **don't have** .... money to buy a sandwich.
4 I **have** / **don't have** .... money to buy a car.
5 There **are** / **aren't** .... recycling bins in my area.
6 ....
7 ....

5 Look at the picture and write sentences. Use *too much/many* and *enough*.

He doesn't have enough money to pay.

Writing

1 Read and circle the examples Harry gives.

My Action Plan

My family produces a lot of trash. Every day we throw out soda cans, plastic bottles, and cardboard packaging. Mom says we don't have enough time to recycle everything.

I want to persuade my family to recycle and reuse our trash. We can reuse water bottles and we can recycle all the cans and packaging.

The things I can do to help are:

- buy some bins and label them glass, plastic, paper, and metal
- help Mom with the trash every day
- upcycle some trash into cool things

2 Think about things your family throw out and answer the questions.

1 What trash do you produce a lot of? Give examples.

....

2 How can you persuade friends/teachers/parents to reduce the amount?

....

3 What can you do to help? Think of three examples.

....

3 Write about your action plan in your notebook. Use your ideas from Activity 2.

(!) Remember

Check (✓) what your writing has.

a writing strategy:
   examples ☐

b vocabulary:
   kinds of materials ☐
   household items ☐
   recycling words ☐

c correct spelling: ☐

57

Now I Know

1 Read and match.

1 There are too many empty bottles in the kitchen.
2 I don't have enough bread.
3 There are too many students for one project.
4 There isn't enough flour to make a cake.
5 You don't need to get milk.
6 Could you ask your brothers to help?

a I need to go shopping.
b There's enough milk in the fridge.
c We could do two projects.
d They don't have enough time.
e You could make cupcakes.
f We need to reduce the amount of plastic we use.

2 Write the words in alphabetical order.

> soil   glass jar   natural resources   can   stuff   wood
> cardboard   cup   fleece   tire   toilet paper roll   recycling plant

1 ....
2 ....
3 ....
4 ....
5 ....
6 ....
7 ....
8 ....
9 ....
10 ....
11 ....
12 ....

3 Read and complete. Use the correct form of the words from Activity 2.

1 Mom bought six new coffee ....
2 We need to get new .... for the car.
3 I love my .... sweater. It's so warm!
4 Put the soda .... in the recycling bin.
5 We use .... to make paper.
6 This is the .... we use for candy.
7 We sort trash so they can go to a ...., not a landfill.
8 Peter built his house using .... like stone and wood.

58

4 Read and complete. There's one extra word.

create	decorations	frame	fumes	landfills	metal
process	packaging	plastic	throw	toxic	upcycle

1 The .... in the air are ....
2 We should stop filling .... with trash, such as .... and ....
3 Don't .... out the .... from the pizza. Recycle it.
4 You can .... these bottle caps and .... something new.
5 These party .... and this picture .... are made from paper.

5 Read the problems and suggest solutions.

1 I'm going on vacation but I can't take my pet with me.
....
2 I'm using too many plastic bottles.
....

Things I learn

1 Write down your three favorite new words from this unit. Which word was the most difficult?
....

2 Write two things you found interesting about:

1 upcycling
....

2 recycling
....

3 Why do people produce so much trash?
....

5 How can we choose our jobs?

1 What jobs do you know? What would you like to learn about jobs?

....

....

2 Circle the words related to work. What else do you think you will learn about jobs?

bus   doctor   practice   sky   study   talent   teacher

....

3 🎬 5-1 BBC Watch the video. Match the words to make phrases.

1 space   a cards
2 children's   b shavings
3 greeting   c books
4 pencil   d glass
5 sea   e Day
6 Mother's   f ships

4 🎬 5-1 BBC Complete the sentences. Use phrases from Activity 3. Watch the video again to check.

1 An illustrator can dream up mountains, dragons, unicorns, ... , and giants.
2 Kirsty wants to illustrate .... and magazines.
3 Kirsty makes glass earrings on her .... card.
4 Ruth uses .... in her designs.
5 Tamira wants to illustrate .... and books.
6 The girls made card designs using ....

60

Reading 1

1 Read *Famous People* and complete the chart.

Famous People

Leonardo da Vinci

Leonardo da Vinci was one of the most important painters of the fifteenth century. His most famous painting is the *Mona Lisa*, a picture of a smiling woman. But Leonardo wasn't just a painter. He was also a scientist and an engineer – he designed a flying machine, a tank and a bridge, and he made drawings of the human body.

Florence Nightingale

Florence Nightingale was the most famous nurse in the nineteenth century. In 1860, she started a famous nursing school in London. Florence was also a writer and a good mathematician. She wrote books on nursing and she was one of the first people to use pie charts to present data.

Louis Armstrong

Louis Armstrong was one of the most famous American jazz musicians of the twentieth century. He played the trumpet; he was famous for his long trumpet solos. He was also a singer and a composer. He wrote more than 50 jazz songs that people still play today.

Rosa Parks

Rosa Parks was one of the most important activists during the civil rights movement in the United States in the 1960s. She's most famous for refusing to give her seat to a white person on a bus. After this she became an activist for equal rights. Before that she was a seamstress in a department store. She also wrote two autobiographies.

	Leonardo da Vinci	Florence Nightingale	Louis Armstrong	Rosa Parks
Famous for …				

2 Read *Famous People* again and write.

1 These people were very creative: ....
2 These people wrote books: ....
3 These people were American: ....
4 These people used math and science in their work: ....

3 Discuss with a friend. Do you know anyone who has a similar job to any of the people in the biographies? Who is it? What do they do?

Vocabulary 1

1 Read and circle.

1 Athletes **train** / **discover** / **compose** in all kinds of weather.
2 Marie Curie **composed** / **trained** / **discovered** new chemical elements.
3 The scientists **competed** / **discussed** / **trained** the results of their work in the lab.
4 A painter needs good light in their **studio** / **lab** / **brush** to see the colors well.
5 Not all musicians **discover** / **compete** / **compose** music for their songs.
6 He **competed** / **trained** / **discussed** in the race but he didn't win. He came second.

2 Read and complete.

athlete   brushes   competes   composes   lab
musician   painter   self-portraits   trains

1 Kelly's an excellent _____. She plays the piano and _____ her own songs.

3 John's a good _____. He _____ every day and _____ in running events at school.

2 Ian wants to be a famous _____. He paints _____. He just got some new _____.

4 Georgina's a scientist. She works in a _____.

3 Think about three famous people from your country. What are their names? What are they famous for?

1 athlete: ....
2 musician: ....
3 painter: ....

Vocabulary challenge: words related to jobs

4 Look, read, and write.

co-worker   salary   meeting   employer   interview

1 the money you get for your work
2 a person you work with
3 the person or company you work for
4 a talk about a work project
5 a talk with someone you hope will give you a job

5 Read and complete. Use the singular or plural form of the words from Activity 4.

1 Soda companies are the .... for a lot of people all over the world.
2 You have to go to a lot of important .... when you work for a big company.
3 Alex and Trisha are .... They work in the same company.
4 It's important to dress smartly for a job ....
5 Most companies pay your .... into your bank account.

63

Grammar 1

Rashid runs **fast**. He runs **faster than** Santiago. He runs **the fastest** in our class.
Holy sings **loudly**. She sings **more loudly** than Dean. She sings **the most loudly** of all.

Jack played **well**. He played **better than** before. He played **the best**.
Roman played **badly**. He played **worse than** before. He played **the worst**.

1. The green words compare two actions.
2. The blue words describe actions.
3. The orange words compare all actions.

1 Read and underline words that describe or compare actions.. Circle the words before them. Then match.

1. We played well today. We played better than yesterday.
2. Olive's a great swimmer. She swims faster than the rest of the group.
3. Jeff did badly in the test. He did worse than in the last test.
4. My sisters sing loudly. I sing the most loudly of all.
5. I think fish smells worse than eggs!

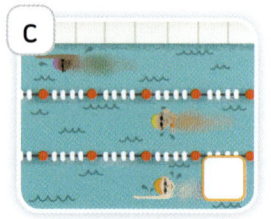

2 Complete the dialog. Use *better*, *worse*, *best*, or *worst*.

Gabe: Hi Sue. What's up?

Sue: Hi. I just started taking piano lessons. Could you help me practice? I think I play the ¹_____ in my class.

Gabe: Sure, I can help you. I'm sure you play ²_____ than me when I started. I was awful!

Sue: Really?! But you played the ³_____ in the last concert.

Gabe: That's because I practice a lot. In my first concert I played ⁴_____ than my younger sister. Even my mom had to cover her ears!

3 🎧 📋 **Listen and check (✓).**
03

1 What's the best job for Ben?

a　　　　　　　　b　　　　　　　　c

2 Which girl is Amy?

a　　　　　　　　b　　　　　　　　c

3 What are Mom and Caleb doing now?

a　　　　　　　　b　　　　　　　　c

4 What's Penny's worst subject?

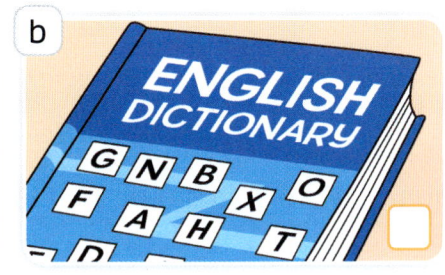

a　　　　　　　　b　　　　　　　　c

4 Write sentences that are true for you.

1 I / my best friend / sing / worse ....
2 my mom / my dad / cook / better ....
3 my grandma / I / draw / better ....
4 ....

Reading 2

A GREAT ADVENTURE

Day 1

Today, we're setting out on our journey. We're going to travel around the world faster than anyone before. I'm so excited, but a bit worried, too. It's going to be a long and dangerous journey, but I have my crew with me and we'll help each other. It'll be a great adventure!

I'm Jack Shaw and I'm the Captain. All 13 members of the crew are younger than me, but they know their job well. All we need is good weather so that we reach our destination the fastest.

Day 10

The weather was perfect for the first few days as we sailed down the coast of Portugal. But on day five, we had a huge storm. Joe, the youngest crew member, was terrified. This is his first journey and he sometimes gets seasick. Susan, our doctor, helps him when he's feeling unwell.

Day 30

We had problems because five members of the crew got sick yesterday. Susan is worried because they can't eat or drink. I'm worried because it's difficult to sail the yacht with only eight crew members.

Day 64

We arrived back in the U.K. at the Lizard Lighthouse on the south-west coast of England. I'm sad because we traveled the slowest and ended up in last place, but I'm happy because we had an amazing adventure and made it home safely.

1 Read *A Great Adventure* and answer the questions.

1. Why was Susan worried? ....
2. How did the Captain feel at the end? ....

2 Read *A Great Adventure* again. Write **T** (true) or **F** (false).

1. The weather was bad at the start of the journey. ....
2. The Captain knew the journey was dangerous. ....
3. The Captain felt good on Day 1. ....
4. Jack is the youngest member of the crew. ....

3 Would you like to sail with Captain Shaw and his crew? Why/Why not?

....

Vocabulary 2

1 Decode the words. Then match them to the pictures.

A	B	C	D	E	F	G	H	I	J	K	L	M	N	O	P	Q	R	S	T	U	V	W	X	Y	Z
1	2	3	4	5	6	7	8	9	10	11	12	13	14	15	16	17	18	19	20	21	22	23	24	25	26

1. SAILOR (19 1 9 12 15 18)
2. EXPLORER (5 24 16 12 15 18 5 18)
3. SURGEON (19 21 18 7 5 15 14)
4. BARBER (2 1 18 2 5 18)
5. JOURNEY (10 15 21 18 14 5 25)
6. CREW (3 18 5 23)

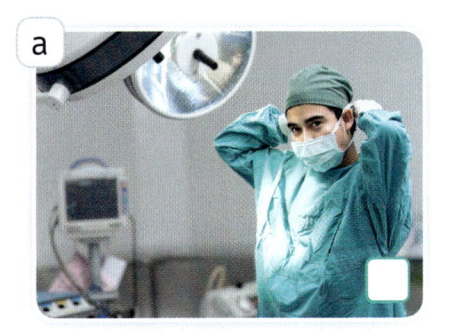

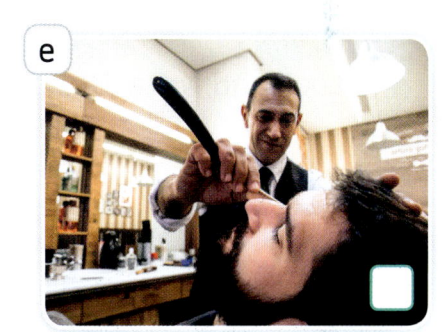

2 Read and circle.

1. We didn't enjoy the flight. It was **terrifying** / **comfortable** because there was a storm.
2. There's the bus! We must run **fast** / **hard** to catch it.
3. It's **delicious** / **late**. I'm going to bed. Goodnight.
4. Mom works **hard** / **fast** every day.
5. This armchair is very **fast** / **comfortable**. Is it new?
6. What's in this soup? It's **terrifying** / **delicious**. Yum!

67

3 Circle the odd one out. Then write sentences with the words you circled.

1	terrifying	delicious	journey	4	barber	terrifying	comfortable
2	explorer	late	sailor	5	delicious	surgeon	sailor
3	surgeon	fast	hard	6	explorer	journey	comfortable

....

....

....

....

Word study: suffixes -er and -or

4 Look and write. Use the verbs from the box with -er and -or.

act   paint   sail   sing   teach

1 2 3 4 5

5 Can you think of more jobs that end in -er or -or? Complete the chart.

-er	-or

Grammar 2

Adverbs describe actions
The firefighters are working **hard**.
They're working **harder than** the reporter.
They're working **the hardest**.

The firefighters work **carefully**.
They work **more carefully than** the reporter.
They work **the most carefully**.

Adjectives describe things
The fire is very **big**.
It's **bigger than** any other fire.
It's **the biggest** fire in Australia.

The photographer has a **difficult** job.
She has a **more difficult** job **than** the reporter.
The firefighters have **the most difficult** job.

1 Read and match.

1 Sloths are
2 Planes travel faster
3 I have to get up earlier
4 I think teachers take school more
5 A clown is funnier than
6 Anja sings more

a seriously than students.
b a firefighter.
c the slowest animals.
d than my younger sister.
e beautifully than me.
f than cars.

2 Read and circle.

1 Sven jumped **the highest** / **higher** of all the students.
2 Lions are more **dangerously** / **dangerous** than mice.
3 My head hurts. Can you speak **more quietly** / **the most quietly**?
4 Tomorrow we'll begin classes **the earliest** / **earlier** than usual.
5 The pink flowers are **the smallest** / **smaller** than the blue flowers.
6 My brother says he works **harder** / **the hardest** than me at school.
7 Millie can run very **fast** / **faster**.
8 Grandma sings **the most** / **more** beautifully in our family.

3 Complete the sentences. Use the correct form of the words from the box.

> difficult   fast   hard   long   quietly   slowly

1 It takes _____ to read a book than to watch a movie.
2 Emily studies the _____ . She always gets the best grades.
3 I think being a firefighter is the _____ job in the world.
4 Kevin is the _____ of my friends. He always wins our races.
5 Can you speak _____ ? I can't understand you.
6 My sister moves _____ than a cat. I never hear her walk into the room.

4 Read and write a comparative and a superlative sentence. Use the words in bold.

1 Ryan laughed **loudly**. Ryan laughed more loudly than Ashley. Ryan laughed the loudest.
2 Doctors work **hard**. _____
3 Ina ate her lunch **quickly**. _____
4 Farmers get up **early**. _____

5 Write comparative and superlative sentences. Use one word from each box.

> be   drive   eat   last   laugh   run   walk

> big   carefully   dangerous   fast   long   loud   quickly

1 _____
2 _____
3 _____
4 _____
5 _____

70

Writing

1 Read and underline the sentences that express the author's opinion.

My Dream Job

My dream job is a scientist. I think a scientist has an important job because they can do something useful for the world. I think I'll be good at my dream job because science is my favorite subject. I also study hard and learn fast. I'd love to meet and discuss my ideas with people who know science better than me. In the future, I want to work in a lab and discover new medicine to help sick people.

2 Think about your dream job. Complete the information.

1 My dream job:
2 Two reasons I like it better than other jobs:

3 One reason why I'll be good at this job:
4 My future plan:

3 Write about your dream job in your notebook. Use your ideas from Activity 2.

⚠ Remember

Check (✔) what your writing has.

a writing strategy:	b vocabulary:	c grammar:	d correct spelling: ☐
my opinion ☐	jobs ☐	adverbs ☐	
reasons ☐		adjectives ☐	

71

Now I Know

1 Complete the crossword.

Across

2 I like to .... my own songs.
4 My uncle is a .... and he works in a hospital.
6 The fastest .... won the race.
9 Hurry up! I don't want to be ....
10 There's a .... on a ship and on a plane.
11 Dad went to the .... to cut his beard.

Down

1 We went on a .... around the world in a yacht.
3 George is an excellent .... He plays the piano well.
5 My aunt is a .... Her pictures of the ocean are beautiful.
7 The .... traveled across the ocean and found a new country.
8 The life of a .... on a ship was very dangerous in the past.

2 Read, write, and circle.

| comfortable   delicious   fast   hard   terrifying |

1 Ten .... athletes are going to **compose** / **compete** in the next race.
2 The chairs in the scientist's **studio** / **lab** aren't ....
3 The explorer **discussed** / **discovered** a .... fruit in the jungle.
4 The painter used a new **crew** / **brush** to paint a picture of a .... storm.
5 The team always **trains** / **composes** very .... before a match.

72

3 Read and complete. There's one extra word.

> better   the best   the worst   well   worse

Hey! Ready for the game? 🙂 We have to play ¹ _____ today to qualify for the finals.

Bad news! I'm sick. I feel much ² _____ than yesterday. 😕😟

Oh, no! We're going to do ³ _____ then ... 😟 You're our star player!

No worries. Matt says he can play and he plays ⁴ _____ in our school.

4 Answer the questions.

1 Who laughs the loudest in your class?
....

2 Who drives more carefully, your mom or dad?
....

3 Who can run faster than you?
....

Things I learn

1 Write down your three favorite new words from this unit. Which word was the most difficult?
....

2 Write two things you found interesting about:

1 the work of an illustrator   2 choosing a job
....
....

3 Why do you think some people have more than one job in their lives?
....

73

6 What happens in extreme conditions?

1 How many types of weather can you name? What else would you like to learn about weather?

....

....

2 Circle the words related to weather. What do you think you will learn about extreme conditions?

beach   climate   frost   island   storm   temperature

....

3 🎬 6-1 BBC Watch the video and circle the correct answer.

1 Wim says he's superhuman because he **trains** / **eats** a lot.

2 Tim's heart beats a lot **slower** / **faster** during the race.

3 The doctor **is** / **isn't** worried about Tim during the race.

4 Tim **doesn't finish** / **finishes** the race.

5 After the race, Tim's **legs** / **feet** hurt the most.

6 After the race, Wim **is** / **isn't** fine.

4 Match the words in bold to their definitions.

1 The Ice Man is **superhuman**.

2 Tim agrees to be a "**guinea pig**".

3 Tim's **heart rate** goes up during the race.

4 When you run in cold weather your heart has to **pump** extremely hard.

5 The human body has an amazing ability to **recover**.

a how fast your heart beats

b to get better after an injury

c force liquid to move somewhere, like blood around a body

d stronger than a regular person

e a person we use for experiments or a small animal

74

Reading 1

1 Read the reviews and circle the correct answers.

JOE'S ENTERTAINMENT BLOG

Check out my recommendations for this week. Here are three reviews.

Book: City of Gold ★★★★★

Francisco de Orellana was a Spanish explorer, and the first person to sail the Amazon River. Orellana and his men wanted to find the lost city of El Dorado, because they thought there was a lot of gold there. They started their journey in February 1542, but they never found the city. They found the Amazon, but Orellana and his men didn't know the dangers they were going to find along the way. This book is amazing.

Movie: The River Journey ★★★★
PG 13

Conditions in the Amazon are really dangerous for a regular city guy like Ted. Ted has a dream – he wants to find El Dorado. Ted soon realizes that this was a bad idea. Lost and suffering from hypothermia, Ted travels down the river, desperate to get home. This exciting motion picture opens in theaters on February 1st.

Documentary: The Amazon ★★★★
Thurs 1/28: 10 p.m.

Nick Ferris goes on a journey down the Amazon River in this excellent four-part documentary. Nick and his crew travel through the biggest forest on Earth and have many incredible adventures. Watch them face extreme dangers, meet the people of the Amazon rainforest, and see new wildlife for the first time. Don't miss part one this Thursday on Channel 9.

The blog has a **short** / **long** / **one sentence** introduction and **one** / **two** / **three** paragraph(s) per review. After the title, Joe included some useful **addresses** / **information** / **costs**.

2 Read the reviews again. Complete the chart.

	City of Gold	The Amazon	The River Journey
1 entertainment type			
2 main character			
3 Joe's opinion			

3 Discuss with a friend. What would you choose to watch or read from the blog? Why?

Vocabulary 1

1 Read and circle.

1 The weather is usually **mild** / **extreme** in North America in the spring.
2 Your body **adapts to** / **shivers** when you're cold because it's trying to warm up.
3 Very cold conditions can cause **heatstroke** / **hypothermia**.
4 When you run, your **heart rate** / **sweat** gets faster.
5 During training, our bodies **perspire** / **beat** more.
6 Terry didn't drink enough water on the trip and he got **numb** / **dehydrated**.

2 Complete the crossword. What's the hidden word? What does it mean?

1 My .... rate is normally 83, but when I exercise it's 110.
2 I'm very thirsty. I think I'm ....
3 When it's hot you .... a lot, so it's important to drink water.
4 It's hard for people from a warm climate to adapt .... the cold weather in the north.
5 It's important to shower so you don't smell of ....
6 I saw you .... Are you cold?
7 It's easy to get .... in the desert because it's so hot.
8 .... heat or cold can kill a person.
9 I can't feel my fingers. They're ....
10 You don't need a coat. The weather is .... today.
11 A doctor listens to your heart .... when you have a health check.

The hidden word is .... It means ....

3 Write the letters in order. Then choose three words and write sentences.

1 r e t e e m x ....
2 p a t a d o t ....
3 t a t r o s h e k e ....
4 e s a t w ....

....
....
....

Vocabulary challenge: weather words

4 Read the sentences and label the pictures with the words in bold.

1 A **sandstorm** is one of the most dangerous things that can happen to you in a desert.
2 We were driving to my grandma's for Christmas but we got stuck in a **blizzard**.
3 Last year the river overflowed and a **flood** hit our town.
4 The air **humidity** is a big problem for people not used to the tropical climate.
5 It hasn't rained for a month and the **drought** has destroyed all our crops.
6 There's a 50 percent chance of **precipitation**, you should take your umbrella.

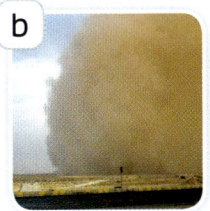

a b c d e f

....

5 Complete the sentences. Use the words from Activity 4.

1 The .... came unexpectedly. We had to go up to the roof to escape the water.
2 I hate this .... In the last month we only had one centimeter of .... and all the plants in my garden are dead.
3 On the first day of winter we were hit by a heavy ....
4 When in a .... cover your mouth and nose so you don't breathe in sand.
5 Most plants in our house like high .... We have to spray them with water.

Grammar 1

I **must** find the Smogator.
You **must** wear gloves, it's cold.

I **have to** take my exams.
You **have to** wear a seat belt.
Do we **have to** finish the project today?

Must expresses obligation that comes from the speaker (not a rule or a law).
Have to expresses obligation that comes from somebody else (can be a rule or a law).

1 Read and check (✓) the sentences that are rules or laws.

1 You have to finish your homework before you go out. ☐
2 We must do something to save our planet. ☐
3 My parents have to go to work. ☐
4 You must visit us when you're in London. ☐

2 Complete the sentences with **must** or **have to** and the verbs from the box. Then match.

hurry up   pass   pay   wear

1 Workers at the construction site .... hard hats.
2 You .... an exam to drive a car.
3 You can't eat it now! You .... first!
4 I .... I don't want to be late.

78

3 Write the words in order.

1 arrive / have / students / at / 8 a.m. / at / school / to

....

2 I / a / buy / sneakers / new / must / of / pair

....

3 late / getting / it's / , / go / I / must / now

....

4 gift / I / must / to / a / for / get / Natalia / remember

....

5 have / wear / to / officers / police / uniforms

....

6 before / home / has / dark / gets / brother / be / to / my / it

....

4 Complete the questions. Then answer for you.

1 .... (wear) a uniform to school? ....
2 .... (stay) at home when it's cold? ....
3 .... (do) homework every day? ....
4 .... (prepare) for extreme weather in your country? ....

5 Write two things you must do and two things you have to do today.

Must	Have to

Reading 2

The Storm

My friend Leyla and I were sitting under a tree in the playground during a break. We were far away from the other children because we were reading our notes for our science test. Suddenly, the birds stopped singing. I don't know why but I knew something was going to happen … and then the rain started!

The other children quickly ran into the school building. "Come on, Vicky!" Leyla shouted. Before we got to the door, we were all wet. I pulled at the door but it didn't open! "Oh no, what are we going to do now?" asked Leyla.

"I don't know," I said, "but this isn't good. Look at the sky!"

The sky was black. It was raining really hard now. Suddenly, lightning lit up the sky and then we heard a loud rumble of thunder. "We've got to get inside!" I shouted. We started to bang on the doors. "Help! Help! Open the doors!"

Luckily, Mr Smith heard us, and he rushed to open the doors. As we ran inside the building, the lightning struck again and we heard a loud crack behind us – it hit the tree in the playground and split it in two! The tree crashed down onto the steps in front of the doors.

"Thank goodness I heard you girls," said Mr Smith. We stared in shock at the branches on the steps and I thanked our lucky stars that we were inside.

1 Read *The Storm*. How do we know there's a problem in paragraph 1? Check (✓) the correct answer.

1 The birds stop singing. ☐   2 The girls have a test. ☐   3 The rain starts. ☐

2 Read *The Storm* again and answer.

1 In paragraph 2, we know something bad is happening in the sky. What do Vicky and Leyla say that tells us this?

2 What problem do the girls have in paragraph 3?

3 In which paragraph do we find out that the girls are safe? Which sentences tell us they're safe?

3 Imagine Mr. Smith doesn't open the doors. What should the girls do then?

Vocabulary 2

1 Look and complete.

ash   crater   eruptions   explosion   lava   volcano

1 Vesuvius is an active _____ close to Naples in Italy.
2 On Big Island in Hawaii, hot _____ flows into the ocean.
3 Sometimes the _____ of a volcano fills with water forming a lake, like in Quilotoa in Ecuador.
4 In 2017, _____ rose high into the sky from the island Anak Krakatau in Indonesia.
5 In Iceland, there are _____ of gas and steam from the ground every day.
6 The last _____ from Mount Etna injured ten people.

2 Complete the text. Use the words from Activity 1.

There was once a mountain on an island. It wasn't a regular mountain – it was a ¹_____. The local people called it Big Jack. One day, a loud ²_____ came from the mountain. "Oh, no!" everyone shouted. "It's an ³_____. Run!" Everyone ran to the beach. They could see red hot ⁴_____ and black clouds of ⁵_____ coming from Big Jack.

Big Jack was active for one week, but the islanders were safe by the sea. When Big Jack went quiet again, all that was left was a large ⁶_____. The mountain disappeared, so now, Big Jack is called Little Jack.

3 Circle the odd one out. Then write sentences with the words you circled.

1 crater   volcano   medallion
2 safe   eruption   explosion
3 in danger safe   shake
4 tremor   lava   volcano
5 shake   collapse   in danger
6 lava   ash   collapse

....
....
....
....
....

Word study: words of French origin

4 Write the letters in order. Use the definitions to help you.

1	n g e d a r	....	(noun):	a situation where you can get hurt or die
2	m e a l l i o d n	....	(noun):	a metal disk you wear on a chain around your neck
3	t i c u n	....	(noun):	a piece of clothing that doesn't usually have sleeves
4	s t g e r a n	....	(adjective):	weird or unusual
5	a n d a b o n	....	(verb):	leave a place permanently
6	e a p e s c	....	(verb):	get free or get into safety

5 Complete the sentences. Use the words from Activity 4.

1 Roman men wore .... and sandals.
2 I like the .... you're wearing. Is it gold or silver?
3 Some people say that birds can sense ....
4 I keep my dog on a leash when I walk him, so he doesn't ....
5 During a disaster, many people have to .... their homes.
6 A modern city would be a very .... place for a person from the past.

Grammar 2

> It's your decision. You **don't have to** go to the party.
> At the weekend, I **don't have to** go to school!
>
> You **mustn't** run across the street.
> We **mustn't** shout in class.
>
> *Mustn't* means prohibition and *don't have to* is just lack of obligation.

1 Read the dialog and choose the correct answer. There's one extra sentence.

1 **Paul:** We don't have to do any homework tonight. It's Friday.
  Daisy: ....
2 **Paul:** We can go to my house and play video games.
  Daisy: ....
3 **Paul:** Why?
  Daisy: ....
4 **Paul:** Oh, too bad. How about tomorrow?
  Daisy: ....

a I have to help Mom clean the house.
b Yes, you're right. Do you have any plans for tonight?
c Sure, I don't have to do chores tomorrow.
d OK. But usually I have to remind you.
e Sorry. I mustn't be home late.

2 Read Mom's note. Circle and write.

| call | cook | go | have |

1 Lee **must / mustn't** .... to the shop to get bread.
2 He **doesn't have to / must** .... his supper.
3 He **mustn't / doesn't have to** .... his dad before 7 p.m.
4 He **must / mustn't** .... more than one donut.

Hi Lee,
Please buy some bread.
Don't worry about cooking – your supper is in the oven.
Please don't call Dad before 7 p.m., he has an important meeting.
Don't eat all the donuts. There's one for everyone! Love you!
Mom xxx

83

3 Look and write. Complete the sentences. Use *doesn't have to* or *mustn't* and the verbs in bold.

1 clean / go

Eric .... his room. It's tidy. Mary .... to sleep before she puts her toys away.

2 do / play

Mary .... homework because she's only six. Eric .... loud music because it's evening.

3 watch / worry

Eric .... TV before he finishes studying. Mary is learning to read, but she .... about new words because her dad is helping her.

4 Write sentences. Use *don't have to* or *mustn't* and a phrase from the box.

> go for a trip to a volcano   sit in the sun all day   take an umbrella
> walk outside without shoes

1 It never rains here in the summer. You ....
2 You'll get heatstroke. You ....
3 You'll hurt your feet. You ....
4 If you're scared you ....

5 Write two things you mustn't do and two things you don't have to do at home.

1 ....
2 ....
3 ....
4 ....

Writing

1 Read and underline the most important information in the episode summary.

Ocean Trip

Episode 3

This week, the team are in the Pacific Ocean and they must get to Hawaii. The wind is dangerous but they mustn't panic. One member of the team hurts his arm, but the captain quickly helps him. The team get tired, but they have to work for many days and survive the extreme conditions. They also have to survive without a lot of sleep. Will they arrive safely in Hawaii? You must watch this exciting episode to find out!

2 Think about a nature show you like. Write down information about your favorite episode.

1 Title: ....
2 Episode: ....
3 Place: ....
4 Transportation: ....
5 Problems: ....

3 Write the summary of the episode you chose in your notebook. Use the information from Activity 2.

(!) Remember

Check (✔) what your writing has.

a writing strategy: information from the internet/books ☐
b vocabulary: weather words ☐ extreme conditions ☐
c grammar: *must/have to* ☐
d correct spelling: ☐

Now I Know

1 Write the letters in order. Then write the words in the correct word groups.

1 s a h ....
2 a c r r t e ....
3 y d d h r a d t e e ....
4 t i u p o n e r ....
5 h e o r y p m i a t h ....
6 v a a l ....
7 b n m u ....
8 s e p e r i r p ....
9 e v s i h r ....
10 w e a t s ....
11 m o r e t r ....
12 o l v n o c a ....

Human body	Natural world

2 Read and circle.

Danny: It's freezing outside. We ¹ **must / mustn't** wear our gloves and scarves.

Olivia: You're right. We ² **have to / don't have to** be careful. Last winter we almost got hypothermia.

Danny: I remember. It was terrible. We ³ **must / mustn't** do that ever again.

Olivia: Let's build a snowman here. Do we ⁴ **have to / must** use a carrot for its nose? I don't think we have one.

Danny: No. We ⁵ **don't have to / mustn't** use a carrot. We can find a stone or stick instead.

3 Read and complete.

| adapt | ash | beats | danger | heatstroke | rate |

1 A normal heart .... is from 60 to 100 .... a minute.
2 You can get .... when you don't .... to a hot climate.
3 Volcanic .... in the sky can put planes in ....

4 Write sentences that are true for you.

1 go shopping after school
   I don't have to go shopping after school.

2 lie to my parents
   ....

3 clean my room today
   ....

4 return books to the library on time
   ....

Things I learn

1 Write down your three favorite new words from this unit. Which word was the most difficult?

....

2 Write two things you found interesting about:

1 the effects of extreme weather on people   2 places with extreme weather

....
....

3 Why do people want to travel to places with extremely hot or cold weather?

....

87

7 How and why do fashions change?

1 What items of clothing are you wearing? What would you like to learn about clothes?

....

....

2 Circle the words related to fashion. What do you think you will learn about fashion?

chair   honey   mechanic   pattern   show   silk

....

3 🎬 BBC Watch the video and complete.

This week's episode is about fashion ¹ d............... . Dylan and Izzie are in ² L............... – the capital of the British fashion industry. They meet Giles, who tells them that you have to work ³ h............... in the fashion industry. Watch Dylan and Izzie ⁴ p............... their own designs and see how they react when they see them on actual ⁵ m............... .

4 🎬 BBC Complete the sentences. Watch the video again to check.

lace   outfits   overlaps   show   touches   vision

1 Dylan likes to match ....
2 Giles tells Izzie and Dylan it's important to have their own distinctive ....
3 Izzie and Dylan's pieces will be presented on the runway in a fashion ....
4 The children add the finishing .... to their pieces themselves.
5 Izzie puts .... on the neck area of her yellow shirt.
6 Dylan .... the material on his jacket to make a zebra design.

Reading 1

1 Look and read *Fashion Through the Centuries*. Label the pictures with the correct century.

Fashion THROUGH THE CENTURIES

Extravagant hats were very popular in the fifteenth century. Women's hats were often tall with long silk fabric on them. Men could choose from a wide variety of wool or felt hats. Women's dresses and men's cloaks were very long and they were made of wool. Blue was a new color to Europe and it was very fashionable.

In the sixteenth century, women's dresses were long, wide, and heavy. Women wore hoops under their dresses to make them wide. These dresses were made of thick fabric and they also had a white collar called a ruff. Men also wore ruffs around their necks and soft caps on their heads. They wore tight-fitting jackets. Their pants were very short, and they also wore tights.

A century later, women wore long silk dresses which had puff sleeves. Men still wore knee-length pants. They also wore knee-high boots, wide hats, and linen capes. Lace was very popular for men and women. Men tied lace scarves around their necks and they also wore long, curly wigs.

2 What did men and women wear in each century? Read *Fashion Through the Centuries* again and write.

15th century
Men: .... Women: ....

16th century
Men: .... Women: ....

17th century
Men: .... Women: ....

3 Which fashion style do you like best? Why?

....
....

Vocabulary 1

1 Find ten words and write them in alphabetical order. Then label the pictures.

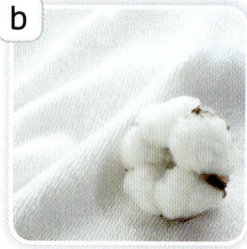

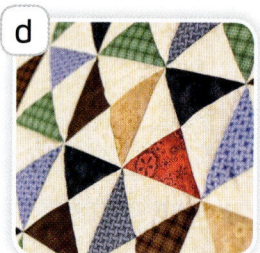

S	D	C	C	C	Y	L	K
U	X	O	W	O	O	L	C
I	U	L	T	T	W	L	C
T	P	L	T	T	L	E	A
S	T	A	O	O	L	A	R
E	I	R	T	N	O	T	D
N	G	L	I	T	H	H	I
T	H	G	K	T	E	E	G
I	T	C	I	R	A	R	A
M	S	D	E	N	I	M	N

1 ....
2 ....
3 ....
4 ....
5 ....
6 ....
7 ....
8 ....
9 ....
10 ....

a .... b .... c .... d .... e ....

2 Read and complete.

> artificial fiber   denim   leather   patterns   vest

1 Lycra is a modern .... that makes fabric stretch.
2 .... of flowers on clothes are sometimes fashionable, but they aren't everybody's taste.
3 Wearing a .... with a suit creates a smarter look.
4 .... shoes are very durable and comfortable.
5 .... is a very hard-wearing fabric. It was first worn by laborers before becoming a fashion item for pants and jackets.

3 What clothes and materials should you wear to these occasions?

1 A wedding: ....
2 An afternoon at a park: ....

Vocabulary challenge: fabric patterns

4 Decode the words.

A	B	C	D	E	F	G	H	I	J	K	L	M	N	O	P	Q	R	S	T	U	V	W	X	Y	Z
1	2	3	4	5	6	7	8	9	10	11	12	13	14	15	16	17	18	19	20	21	22	23	24	25	26

1. P L A I D (16 12 1 9 4)
2. S T R I P E D (19 20 18 9 16 5 4)
3. P O L K A D O T (16 15 12 11 1 4 15 20)
4. C A M O U F L A G E (3 1 13 15 21 6 12 1 7 5)
5. F L O R A L (6 12 15 18 1 12)
6. S O L I D C O L O R (19 15 12 9 4 3 15 12 15 18)

5 Look and complete. Use the words from Activity 4. Then design your own outfit in your notebook and write a description.

For this outfit, I chose a [1] .... skirt and I matched it with a [2] .... T-shirt. To add some fun, I chose a green and blue [3] .... pattern for the tights.

....
....

Grammar 1

I had breakfast **before** I went to school.
I went to school **after** I had breakfast.
I had classes **when** I got to school.

1 Read and circle.

I got up five minutes ¹ **when / after** my alarm rang. I had a shower ² **after / when** I was in the bathroom. I got dressed. It was cold, so I put on my cardigan ³ **after / before** I put on my T-shirt and pants. I had cereal for breakfast and I washed my bowl and spoon ⁴ **before / after** I finished. Dad drove me to school. We chatted about soccer ⁵ **before / when** we were in the car. I got to school early – ten minutes ⁶ **before / after** the bell rang.

2 Think about your morning. Complete the sentences for you.

1. I left home _____ I had breakfast.
2. I got dressed _____ I brushed my teeth.
3. I got up _____ my parents got up.
4. I packed my lunch _____ I left for school.

3 Read and complete. Use *before*, *after*, or *when* and a verb from the box.

| booked | crossed | had | parked | played | told |

1. Mom got up _____ she _____ breakfast in the kitchen.
2. Dad locked the car _____ he _____ it at the mall.
3. We went on vacation in June, two months _____ we _____ the trip in April.
4. Our teacher was upset _____ she _____ us we all failed the test.
5. My hands got cold _____ I _____ in the snow without gloves.
6. I looked for cars _____ I _____ the street.

4 William did things differently yesterday. Look and write.

1. eat dessert / eat dinner

4. sit on the table / have breakfast

2. go skateboarding / take off his sneakers

5. put on his T-shirt / put on his sweater

3. put on his pajamas / have supper

6. do his homework / be in bed

5 What else do you think William did differently yesterday? Write sentences. Use *before*, *after*, and *when*.

1
2
3

93

Reading 2

THE SECRET IN THE CELLAR

Iris, Felix and Stefan were at their grandma's house for the weekend. Grandma fell asleep after dinner.

"I'm bored!" said Felix. "What shall we do?"

"I know! Let's explore!"

"Great idea!" said Iris. "There's a door that Grandma always keeps closed. I think it goes down into the cellar! Why don't we go down there and see what we can find?"

"OK. She keeps it locked, but I know where the key is," said Stefan.

He tiptoed into the kitchen, opened the cupboard and found a key in a cup. They opened the door. The cellar was dark.

"We should get a torch. I don't want to fall down the stairs," said Felix.

"Why don't we use the torch on my phone?" suggested Iris and started going down.

There was a light at the bottom and she turned it on. The cellar was empty!

"This is boring. We should go back upstairs," said Felix.

"Hey, guys," said Stefan. "I think I found something under the stairs."

He was holding a dusty box. Inside, there were some old, black and white photos of a magician and his assistant. The assistant was wearing a sparkly dress and she had lots of bracelets on.

"Who is he? And who is that lady?" asked Iris.

A voice behind them answered.

"It's me before I met your grandad. It was my secret!" said Grandma.

"That's the coolest secret ever!" said Felix.

1 Read *The Secret in the Cellar* carefully. Then cover the story and answer the questions.

1. What are the names of the three kids?
2. Where's the key?
3. What do they use on Iris's phone?
4. Where does Stefan find the box?
5. What's in the box?
6. Who thinks Grandma's secret is cool?

2 What do you think happened next? Was Grandma cross? What did Iris and Stefan say? Discuss with a friend and think of an ending to the story.

Vocabulary 2

1 Read and write T (true) or F (false).

1 A person who designs clothes is called an architect. ....
2 Delicate things are easy to destroy. ....
3 We dress up for special occasions. ....
4 You should borrow things without asking first. ....

2 Read, choose, write. There's one extra word.

belt   bracelet   design   earrings   necklace   ribbon   watch

1 This is something you wear around your neck. ....
2 Some people wear this because their pants are too big. ....
3 Little girls like to wear this in their hair. ....
4 These look nice in your ears. ....
5 People wear this to know the time. ....
6 People wear this on their wrists for decoration. ....

3 Write the letters in order. Then use the words to complete the message. There's one extra word.

i e l c d a e t   ....
e e l y w r j   ....
s e r s d p u   ....

o r o r w b   ....
g d d e e n s i   ....
i b r o n b   ....

Advice

Hi Katy! My advice on ¹............ is don't wear anything big and fancy. A ²............ bracelet looks prettier on a young teen. You can ³............ my silver bracelet if you like. It was ⁴............ by my friend. Also, my advice for clothes is ⁵............ ! It's your birthday, so you want to look great! Wear something really nice, like that dress we bought last month.
Love you little sister!

4 Imagine you're a jewelry and accessories designer. Design three things and write a sentence about each.

Word study: phrasal verbs with *take*

5 Read and match.

1 If you don't like this dress, I can **take** it
2 Put the trash bag by the door. I will **take** it
3 Your shoes are dirty. Please **take** them
4 My dad got a new job. He will **take** us
5 Martha is very stubborn. She **takes**

a **off** at the door.
b **back** to the store.
c **after** her mom.
d **away** when I go out.
e **out** to a restaurant to celebrate.

6 Complete the sentences. Use the phrasal verbs from Activity 5.

1 When my cousins visit we often .... them .... for pizza.
2 Let me help you .... your coat, Grandpa.
3 Tim bought a new couch, he needs someone to .... the old one.
4 I .... my dad. We're both very tall and skinny.
5 These boots are too big. I have to .... them .... to the store.

Grammar 2

> **Let's** turn off the lights!
> We **should/could** turn off the lights!
> **Shall I/we** turn off the lights?
> **Should I/we** turn off the lights?
> **Why don't you/we** turn off the lights?

1 Read and circle.

1. Why **do / don't** we get tickets for the show?
2. We're late. We **let's / should** hurry.
3. It's cold. **I shall / Shall I** turn on the heating?
4. It's Mom's birthday tomorrow. **We should / Should we** get her some flowers.
5. We **could / shall** go on vacation to Europe. Do you think the kids would like that?
6. The sales are on. **Let's / Should** go to the mall.

2 Read and complete.

| could | let's | shall | should | why don't |

Fay: Mom, it's Tina's birthday tomorrow. ¹_____ I buy her a gift from the jewelry store?

Mom: That's a good idea. ²_____ go to the mall.

Fay: Cool. We ³_____ look at the clothes stores, too. We might find something there.

Mom: Yes, we could. ⁴_____ we ask Dad to come with us?

Fay: No. He always gets bored at the mall.

Mom: That's true. Well, ⁵_____ we tell him to meet us there at five o'clock? Then we can have pizza together after we shop.

Fay: Great idea!

3 Complete the sentences.

1. _____ go play soccer at the park.
2. _____ I cook fish for dinner? Or do you want something different?
3. _____ we order from this online store? Everything's cheaper there.
4. If you're cold I _____ make you a hot drink.
5. Why _____ you come over? I have a free afternoon.
6. You _____ ask Mom before you buy a leather jacket. They're expensive.

4 The Smith family is going on a picnic. Look at the picture and complete the dialogs.

Shall we take some soda?

No, ...

Let's put tomatoes in the sandwiches.

.... ?

....
....

Yes, we could invite Gemma and Spot, too.

5 Imagine you're going on a picnic with the Smiths. Write five suggestions.

1 ....
2 ....
3 ....
4 ....
5 ....

98

Writing

1 Read and circle the informal greeting and closing phrases. Then underline the suggestions.

From: kylie.e@email.com
To: jan.ine@home.com
Subject: the weekend

Hi Janine,

Let's hang out on the weekend. We could go to the mall in the afternoon for shopping and we could have lunch at that new burger place. We could go to the movies after that. Should we see a comedy or an adventure movie? Why don't we meet at my house at 2 p.m.?

I'm going to wear the new denim pants Mom got me, my favorite cotton shirt, and my leather boots. What about you? You should wear the new necklace and bracelet Brad gave you.

Love,

Kylie

---

2 Think about your plans for the weekend. Write your ideas.

1 Choose a greeting: **Hi** / **Hello**
2 Choose a closing phrase: **Love** / **See you soon**
3 Places to go: ....
4 Things to do: ....
5 Clothes you're going to wear: ....

3 Write an email to a friend about what to do on the weekend in your notebook. Use your ideas from Activity 2.

(!) Remember

Check (✓) what your writing has.

a writing strategy:	b vocabulary:	c grammar:
informal greetings and closing phrases ☐	clothes/jewelry ☐ materials ☐	suggestions ☐ *before/after/when* ☐ d correct spelling: ☐

99

Now I Know

1 Read and circle.

1 We closed our umbrellas a few moments **after** / **before** / **when** the rain stopped.
2 I was asleep **after** / **before** / **when** you called. That's why I didn't answer.
3 Our teacher tested our vocabulary **after** / **before** / **when** I learned the words. I did badly.
4 I heard a loud noise **after** / **before** / **when** the plane flew over. It was enormous!
5 Dad missed the train. He arrived at the station one minute **after** / **before** / **when** it left.

2 Find and circle seven words. Then read and complete.

sbeltknecklacegjewelrywiribbonbebraceletqwatcheeearrings

1 Grandpa says he has to wear a _____ to keep his pants up!
2 That's a lovely _____ you're wearing around your neck.
3 I don't wear a _____. I look at my phone to see the time.
4 You can tie your hair back with a pink or a blue _____.
5 I like the fabric _____ on your arm. Did you make it yourself?

3 Read and complete.

| artificial fibers | borrow | collar | cotton | delicate |
| designed | dress up | leather | pattern | tights |

"Welcome to our fashion show! Our first model is wearing a pair of cool ¹_____ shorts – perfect for the summer – with a classic brown ²_____ belt. Next is the fun look with purple ³_____ – they're made of a comfortable stretch fabric with ⁴_____ including Lycra. Check out the striped ⁵_____. And now our party number – perfect for when you want to ⁶_____ for a special event. This gorgeous dress is made of a ⁷_____ lace fabric, with a pretty ⁸_____ around the neck. It was specially ⁹_____ for this show. And believe me, all your friends will want to ¹⁰_____ this one!"

4 Complete the suggestions.

1. .... meet after school.
2. OK. We .... go to the skateboard park.
3. I don't have my skateboard. .... we go by my house and get it?
4. Sure. .... don't we leave our bags there?
5. OK. We .... ask Steve to come, too. I'll text him.

5 Read and answer. Write full sentences.

1. What are you going to do after school?

   ....

2. What clothes should you wear when it's cold outside?

   ....

3. When should you dress up?

   ....

Things I learn

1 Write down your three favorite new words from this unit. Which word was the most difficult?

....

2 Write two things you found interesting about:

1. how fashion has changed since the 1500s
2. why different materials and patterns are important in fashion

....

3 Why do some people keep old clothes and jewelry instead of throwing them away?

....

101

8 How has entertainment developed?

1 What do people your age do for fun? What else would you like to learn about entertainment?

....

....

2 Circle the words related to entertainment. What do you think you will learn about entertainment?

boring   creative   fun   impossible   perform   rhythm   subway   sword

....

3 🎬 BBC Watch the video and circle the correct answer.
8-1

1 Adam is a **blogger** / **teacher**.
2 He shows us how to create **comics** / **animations**.
3 You start off with a **software programme** / **pencil and paper**.
4 You record the voices **before** / **after** you do the animation on your computer.
5 It's a good idea to draw on **one layer** / **different layers**.
6 You can add music **before** / **after** you import the voice recordings.

4 🎬 BBC Complete the sentences. Watch the video again to check.
8-1

> animated cartoons   animation programme   lip sync
> recording software   sound effects   voice recording

1 You animate your character's mouth to .... with the .... you made.
2 You record your voice with .... and you create the animation with an ....
3 Your .... will be more fun if you add some music and ....

102

Reading 1

1 Read the first paragraph of *Hoop Dancing*. What do the underlined phrases tell us? Check (✓).

1. The writer's opinion about hoop dancing. ☐
2. The most important information about hoop dancing. ☐
3. Some extra facts about traditions. ☐

Hoop Dancing

This week we're looking at <u>hoop dancing</u>. You can probably twirl a hoop around your waist, arms or legs, but can you do it to music? We can see <u>traditional</u> hoop dancing in some <u>Native American tribes</u>, and you might also see <u>hoop dancing performances</u> in <u>rhythmic gymnastics</u>. There are even <u>exercise classes</u> using <u>hoops</u>. They're a bit heavier, but it looks good fun!

Modern Native American hoop dancing is a show dance. In a dance with four hoops, the music and steps are fast. But when a dancer has about 20 hoops, the steps and the drumbeat are slower. The performers twirl the hoops on their arms and legs, and their movements make shapes with the hoops.

In rhythmic gymnastics, groups of gymnasts perform together with hoops and they have to follow rules. The hoop mustn't weigh less than 300g and the gymnasts must twirl the hoops around their hands and bodies while they roll. They can also throw the hoop high and jump and catch the hoop.

The exercise hoops can weigh between 450g and 900g. To get a good workout, you twirl the hoop around your waist and move your hips. It only takes 30 minutes, three times a week to improve your fitness.

2 Read *Hoop Dancing* again and complete the summary.

The article describes three styles of hoop dancing: Native ¹ A_____, rhythmic gymnastics, and exercise ² c_____. In the first style, a ³ d_____ has a lot of ⁴ h_____ and he twirls them at a different pace around his arms or ⁵ l_____. The next style is a competition with ⁶ r_____ for the hoop and the movements. In the final style, you twirl a hoop around your ⁷ w_____ to get a workout.

3 💡 Think about a book you're reading or you've recently read. Write the most important information about it.

1 ....
2 ....

Vocabulary 1

1 🎧 Which is each person's favorite type of music or dance? Listen and match.

1 sister ☐   2 parents ☐   3 daughter ☐   4 son ☐   5 brother ☐

a   b   c   d   e   f

2 Read and complete.

| rhythm   audience   samba |

1 The .... loved the fast .... of the ....

| ballet   hip-hop   hiplet™ |

2 .... is a dance style that combines classical .... and modern .... movements.

3 What's your favorite dance group or dancer? What kind of dance do they perform? Draw or stick a picture and write two sentences about them.

Vocabulary challenge: types of songs

4 Read, look, and write.

1 .... : a song that two people sing together

2 .... : a quiet song that you sing to a baby to help him/her sleep

3 .... : a song for a sports team or for a country

4 .... : a song that, traditionally, a man sings for a woman, often with a guitar

5 .... : a song that a person sings in an opera

6 .... : a song that one person sings

solo

lullaby

duet

aria

anthem

serenade

5 Complete the sentences. Use the words from Activity 4.

1 The baby can't sleep, let's sing her favorite ....
2 Ladies and gentlemen! Please all stand up for our national .... !
3 Will you sing a .... with me? I don't like singing alone.
4 My mom often tells a story about my dad singing a .... under her balcony.

Grammar 1

> **What about** going to a concert tonight?   Yes, let's do that!
> **How about** eating some pizza for dinner?   That's a great idea!

1   Read and circle. Then match.

1 What about **listen / listening** to some rock music?
2 How **about / to** seeing the new *Batman* movie?
3 **Where / What** about getting a takeout?
4 How about **taking / to taking** dance classes before the wedding?
5 What **around / about** watching the dance show on TV?
6 How about **can do / doing** the jive?

a That's a great idea. I'm hungry.
b No thanks. I prefer hip-hop.
c OK. I love dance shows.
d Yes, let's book tickets.
e Sure. Let's do this!
f Good idea. Let's learn the waltz.

2   Read, choose, and write suggestions.

> bake a cake   ~~buy tickets~~   invite friends
> learn to play the guitar   take dance classes

1 There's a dance performance at the theater.
   How about buying some tickets?

2 It's your mom's birthday.
   ....

3 You want to join a band, but you can't sing.
   ....

4 You want to learn the samba.
   ....

5 You don't like going to the movies alone.
   ....

The concert **is starting** at eight o'clock.
My sister **is performing** in a show on Sunday.
I **am meeting** my friend outside the arts center.
Are you **meeting** your grandparents on Sunday?

3 Read and complete. Use the correct form of the verbs in parentheses.

1 We _____ (visit) our friends after school.
2 My brother's band _____ (perform) tonight at 8:30 p.m.
3 Ted and Janet _____ (come over) in the afternoon. Let's order pizza!
4 My aunt _____ (drive) me to school tomorrow because my mom can't.
5 _____ Mom _____ (go) to dance class this evening?
6 Where _____ you _____ (meet) Wesley?

4 Complete the questions. Then answer for you.

1 _____ (you/perform) in the school show this year? _____
2 _____ (your friend/stay) over at your house this weekend? _____
3 _____ (your school/have) a singing competition this year? _____
4 _____ (you/go) to the movies tomorrow? _____
5 _____ (you/visit) your grandma this weekend? _____
6 _____ (your mom/bake) cupcakes in the afternoon? _____

5 Think about your plans for this week. Write what you're doing.

1 I _____ tonight.
2 I _____ this weekend.
3 _____
4 _____
5 _____
6 _____

107

Reading 2

1 Read *The Young Director*. How do we know that Mrs. Fry's the English teacher?

THE YOUNG DIRECTOR

Carlos got up early. He got dressed and put his books in his backpack. He had drama, English, P.E., and history on Mondays. He loved English and writing stories, and he loved drama, but he really enjoyed the things that combined the two. Carlos wanted to be a writer and a director. "I'll go to London and I'll be famous when I'm older," Carlos dreamed.

"Carlos! Hurry up! You don't want to be late for school!" his mom shouted from downstairs.

Drama was the first period. Carlos was surprised to see his drama teacher and his English teacher enter the classroom. "Good morning, class," said Mr. Martin, the drama teacher. "We're combining drama and English today because we have an exciting project for you."

"That's right," said Mrs. Fry. "There's a movie competition next month. Last week, Carlos wrote a movie script for his English project and, with his permission, we'd like to use it."

"Sure!" said Carlos.

"Can Carlos be the director, too? It's his dream," asked his friend, Sara.

Over the next few days, the students learned their lines. On Saturday, the students and teachers met at school and shot the movie. Carlos chose the best angles for the camera and he also gave advice to the actors. On Monday afternoon, Mrs. Fry helped Carlos edit the movie on a computer, and she uploaded it to the competition website. A month later, the principal made an announcement.

"Congratulations grade 3A. You won the movie competition!"

Carlos was so excited. "It's a dream come true!" he said.

2 Read *The Young Director* again and complete the sentences.

1. We know Carlos gives permission to use his script because he says, " _____ ".
2. We know Mrs. Fry can use a computer because she _____ .
3. We know Carlos is happy because he says, " _____ ".

3 Discuss with a friend.

1. Do you think Carlos was a good director? Why?
2. Imagine you have to write a script for a movie. What's it about?

Vocabulary 2

1 Complete the words. Then look and match.

1 _ _ i _ _ n
2 _ _ _ _ _ t _
3 _ _ r _ _
4 c _ _ _ _
5 a _ _ _ _ u _ _
6 _ m _ _ _

2 Read and circle.

1 We loved the **comedy / action / edited** movie. It was very exciting.
2 My cousin is great at drawing. He makes his own 3D **action / horror / animation**.
3 The actors in the **make-up / play / lines** were very talented.
4 At the end everyone clapped. The **applause / animation / drama** was really loud.
5 The **directors / make-up / lines** of big Hollywood movies make a lot of money.
6 Actors use **edit / make-up / action** so they look good on camera.

3 Find and circle six words. Then read and complete.

editqwrealityTVyhcomedyzxlinescbhorrormjdrama

1 I don't like _____ movies. They're too scary for me.
2 Phil saw a great _____ last night. He couldn't stop laughing.
3 One of the actors in the play forgot his _____. He was very embarrassed.
4 Oh, look! Your favorite book was made into a TV _____.
5 We finished filming the movie. Can you help us _____ it?
6 I saw your dad on TV! He was in one of those _____ shows about doctors, wasn't he?

4 Rank the kinds of entertainment from the one you like the most (1) to the one you like the least (7). Then choose four and write why you like/don't like them.

action ☐   animation ☐   comedy ☐   drama ☐
horror ☐   play ☐   reality TV ☐

1 ....
2 ....
3 ....
4 ....

Word study: prefixes *un-* and *im-* for opposites of adjectives

5 Circle the adjectives in the questions. Write their opposites in the answers.

un-

1
Are the tickets for Beyoncé's show available yet?

I'm sorry. They're .... We sold out immediately!

2
Do you think ballroom dancing is popular with your generation?

No. I think it's quite ....

3
Are you enthusiastic about the school dance show?

I am, but a lot of students are .... because they don't like dancing.

im-

4
Do you think this move for our hip-hop routine is possible?

No way! It's totally .... !

5
Were you polite when you asked the actor for an autograph?

Yes. But he was .... and refused to give me one.

6
You must be patient. We're going to the theater tomorrow, not today.

I know. But I'm an .... person! I can't wait to see the play!

Grammar 2

> I**'m meeting** my best friend after school.
> My grandma **is visiting** us next week.
> We use Present Progressive to talk about definite future arrangements.
>
> The concert starts at 1:00 p.m. I**'ll buy** the tickets online now.
> Those bags are too heavy, Mom. I**'ll help** you.
> We use *will* for spontaneous decisions.

1 Read and circle. Then check (✔) the sentences that are spontaneous decisions.

1. Oh no, the car is broken. I guess **I'll take** / **I'm taking** the bus to work. ☐
2. **I'll take** / **I'm taking** a short vacation next week. ☐
3. Amanda **will start** / **is starting** her new job next Monday. ☐
4. I'm hungry. **I'll eat** / **I'm eating** an apple. ☐

2 Read and match.

1. It's hot in here.
2. Dave's band is playing on Sunday.
3. Jack and Katie are going out on Saturday.
4. Martin can't come with us.
5. Tanya invited me for a coffee.

a. I'm meeting her at nine o'clock.
b. I'll call Tod now and invite him instead.
c. I'll open a window.
d. I already have a ticket!
e. They booked a table at that new restaurant.

3 Complete the dialog. Use Present Progressive or *will*.

Tyler: Could you teach me the new move?

Nadine: OK. ¹ _____ (I/show) you. Watch.

Tyler: That looks easy. ² _____ (I/try) it. How's that?

Nadine: Not bad, but you have to practice. ³ _____ (we/do) two dances in the competition next week and this movement is great for the jive.

Tyler: I agree. ⁴ _____ (we/perform) last, so we must amaze the judges.

Nadine: I know. Let's try it again with music.

Tyler: Good idea. ⁵ _____ (Tony/turn) it on. Tony? Music, please!

4 Read and complete. Use the correct form of the words in parentheses. Then match.

1 The phone's ringing! I _____ (answer) it.
2 We _____ (go) for a vacation in Europe next week.
3 Don't worry, I _____ (help) you study for the test.
4 Alfredo _____ (move) to a new apartment tomorrow.
5 Olga and Frank _____ (meet) at 8.00 p.m.
6 **Ellie:** Can I have a soda?
   Matt: Sure, I _____ (get) you one.

a   c   e
b   d   f

5 Read and complete.

> bake a cake   catch the bus   fly to New York
> meet at seven thirty   take an umbrella

1 It's raining now and Francis wants to go out. He _____
2 Anne asked her friend to the movies tonight. They _____
3 My mom's a stewardess. On Monday, she _____
4 Iris is late for school and there isn't time to walk. She _____
5 We just found out our grandparents are visiting tomorrow. We _____

Writing

1 Read the review and underline the opinions.

NIGHT

My favorite series is called *Night* and it's on TV every Saturday. It's about three friends who always hang out together. When one friend keeps disappearing at night, her friends start to follow her to a beautiful fantasy world. It's an action show but it's also funny. In the show there's a lot of modern music, such as hip-hop and rock. My favorite character is Marta, because she always knows how to get out of tricky situations. I think this show is funny and exciting, but sometimes it's scary. You should definitely watch this show!

★★★★★

2 Think about a show or a movie you like and complete the information.

1 Title: ....
2 Characters: ....
3 Plot: ....
....
....
4 Adjectives to describe the show: ....

3 Write your review in your notebook. Use your ideas from Activity 2.

(!) Remember

Check (✓) what your writing has.

a writing strategy:
descriptions ☐
my opinion ☐

b vocabulary:
kind of show/movie ☐
kind of music ☐

c correct spelling: ☐

113

Now I Know

1 Complete the chart. Write the words in alphabetical order.

| hiplet™ | action | waltz | reality TV | ballet | director | hip-hop | horror |
| samba | drama | jive | animation | lines | comedy | tango | rock |

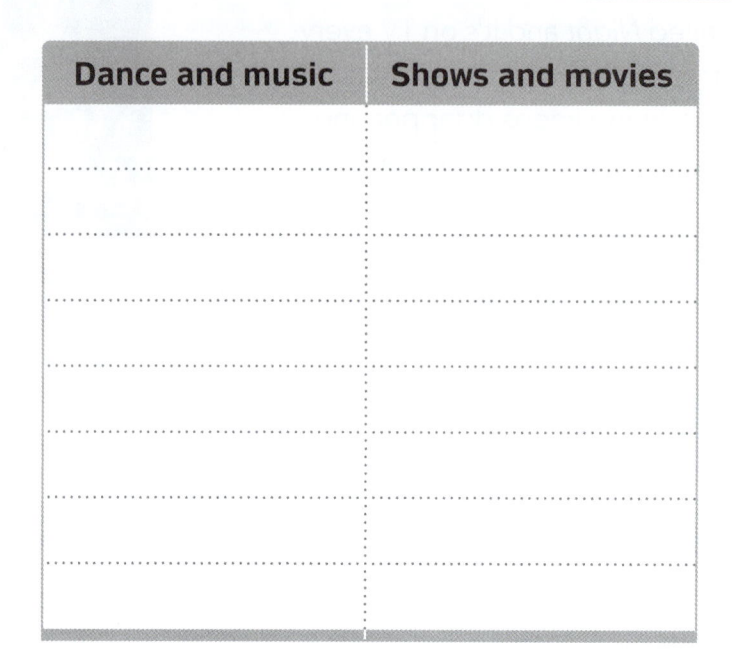

Dance and music	Shows and movies

2 Read and complete.

1 The show was great and the actors' p_____ was excellent.
2 The a_____ loved the show and they stood up and clapped at the end.
3 Dilan would like to take up b_____ dancing as a new hobby.
4 Dancers have to listen to the r_____ of the music and keep to the beat.

3 Write the words in order. Use the verbs in the correct form.

1 eat / tonight / about / how / out

....?

2 about / play / to / see / go / new / the / how

....?

3 school / what / after / about / games / play / board

....?

114

4 Read and complete. Use the words in parentheses and Present Progressive or *will*.

1 Anshu is really excited because she .... (see) *Mamma Mia* on Saturday.
2 Dan doesn't have enough money to get a ticket, but I .... (buy) him one.
3 I'm sorry, I can't talk right now. I .... (call) you later.
4 Joy and Dustin .... (perform) the tango in today's competition. Let's give them a warm welcome!

5 Think about and write five things that you, your family, or friends have planned for next week.

1 ....
2 ....
3 ....
4 ....
5 ....

Things I learn

1 Write down your three favorite new words from this unit. Which word was the most difficult?

....

2 Write two things you found interesting about:

1 different kinds of entertainment

....

2 people who work in entertainment

....

3 Why do people enjoy music, dancing, and movies so much? Which kind of entertainment is your favorite?

....

9 Why are adventure stories popular?

1 What adventure stories do you know? What would you like to learn about them?

....

....

2 Circle the words related to adventures. What do you think you will learn about adventure stories?

amazing   challenge   newspaper   permission   soda   yacht

3 🎬 9-1 BBC Watch the video. Read and check (✔) the true sentences.

1 Blackbeard wasn't very famous. ☐
2 Blackbeard's real name was Edmund Reach. ☐
3 The pirate flag is called the Jolly Roger. ☐
4 Red flag meant danger. ☐
5 Black flag meant that the ship was friendly. ☐
6 Blackbeard didn't tell anyone where he kept his treasure. ☐

4 🎬 9-1 BBC Read and complete. Watch the video again to check.

crew   fleet   frighten   horrible   pirates   returned   smoke

Blackbeard was one of the most famous ¹.......................... of the eighteenth century. He sailed the Atlantic Ocean with his ².......................... and a ³.......................... of ships. He put burning rope in his ears to make them ⁴.......................... . He did this to ⁵.......................... other sailors. Blackbeard was a ⁶.......................... pirate. He left his men on an island and never ⁷.......................... for them.

116

Reading 1

1 Read *Sailing Solo Around the Globe*. Match the headings to the paragraphs.

1 Two around-the-world adventures!
2 Nineteenth-century hero.
3 The fastest voyage.
4 Racing for money.
5 Only three stops!

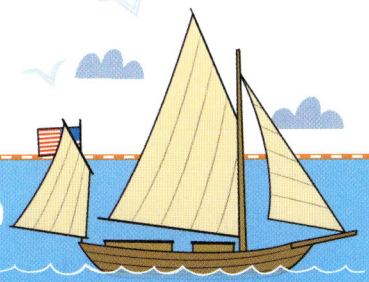

Sailing Solo Around the Globe

A ☐

On April 24, 1895, Joshua Slocum sailed away from Boston Harbor in his boat, *The Spray*. Three years later he returned, after sailing 74,060 kilometers and becoming the first man to sail solo around the world. He visited many exciting places on his voyage, which he later wrote about in his famous book, *Sailing Alone Around the World*.

B ☐

Harry Pidgeon was an American sailor. He was the second person to sail around the world solo – but he was the first person to do it twice. For both voyages he used a boat which he built himself. He left for his first voyage on November 18, 1921, from the Marquesas Islands and it took him almost four years to return to Los Angeles.

C ☐

In June 1942, Argentinian sailor Vito Dumas left Buenos Aires to sail single-handed around the southern oceans. It wasn't a voyage around the world as he didn't sail in the northern oceans, but he sailed longer distances without stopping at land than anyone before. He docked at land three times on a voyage of 32,200 kilometers.

D ☐

Francis Chichester was a British sailor who raced boats. At the age of 65 he decided to sail solo around the world as fast as possible. In 1966, he set off from Plymouth in the U.K. and sailed to Sydney, Australia, where he stopped for 48 days. He returned to Plymouth 274 days after leaving. It was the fastest journey around the world!

2 Read *Sailing Solo Around the World* again and match. Then write the letter of the heading that has the information.

1 Harry Pidgeon
2 Francis Chichester
3 Joshua Slocum
4 Vito Dumas

a 's journey took 274 days. ☐
b wrote a book about his adventures. ☐
c didn't sail in the northern oceans. ☐
d built his boat himself. ☐

3 💬 Discuss with a friend. Which of the sailors would you like to join on their trip? Why?

Vocabulary 1

1 Read and circle. Then match.

1. Finally, the storm cleared and they sailed across a calm, **moonlit / treacherous** ocean again.

2. The **loneliness / yachtsman** arrived back to a hero's welcome.

3. The sailors' most serious problem was **nonstop / exhaustion**. There was no time to sleep.

4. The boat is going to **sink / battle**! We have to swim!

5. When the radio broke, the worst problem for Jim was the **loneliness / endurance**.

6. The winner of the race sailed **nonstop / treacherous** around the world in 90 days.

2 Read and complete. There's one extra word in each box.

| challenge | endurance | treacherous |

Sailing around the world is a test of a person's ¹ _____. It's the kind of ² _____ that only a brave person can accept.

| battle | navigate | sink |

It used to take years to ³ _____ around the world, but nowadays we can do it in months. We still have to ⁴ _____ all kinds of conditions in the ocean.

| loneliness | solo | treacherous |

While sailing ⁵ _____ in the northern oceans, I faced ⁶ _____ cold weather and at one stage I thought I might freeze.

3 Think and write.

1. What do you think a yachtsman feels before, during, and after a voyage?

   ....

2. Do you think it's safer to sail solo today than in the past? Why?

   ....

Vocabulary challenge: parts of a ship

4 Read, look, and label.

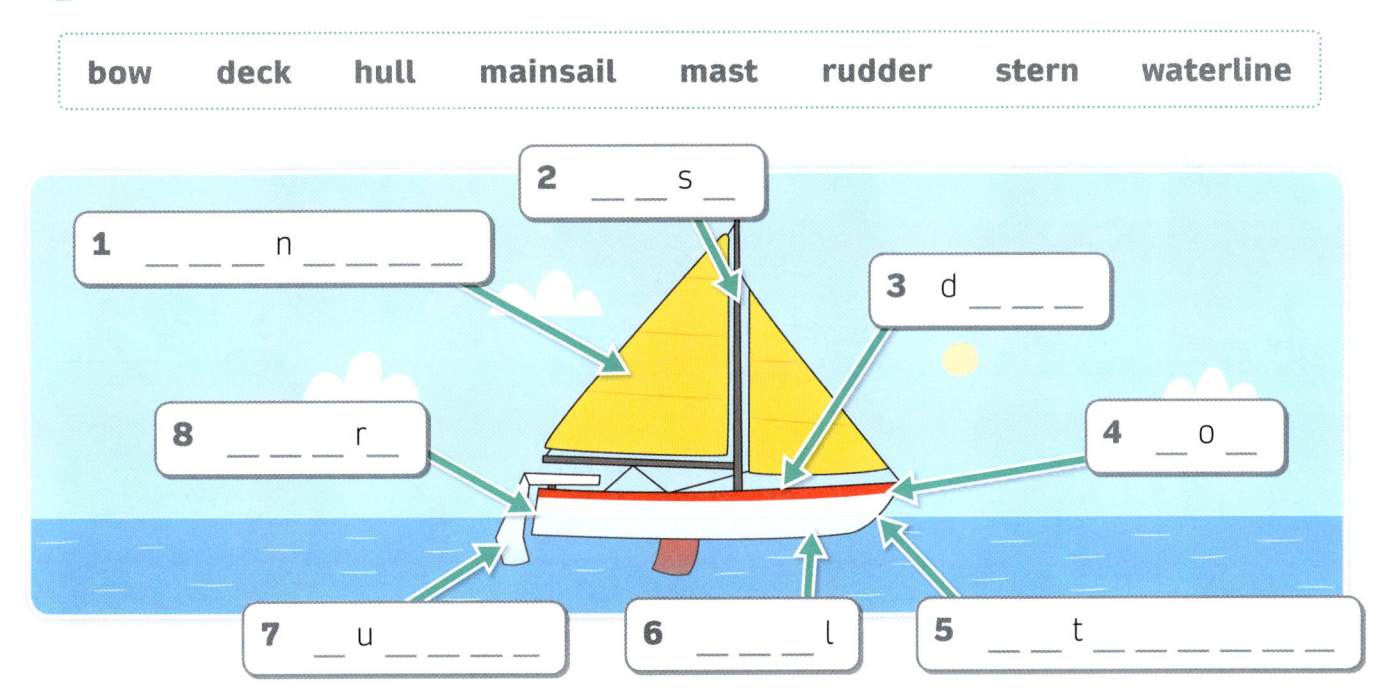

bow   deck   hull   mainsail   mast   rudder   stern   waterline

1. __ __ __ n __ __ __ __
2. __ __ s __
3. d __ __ __
4. __ o __
5. __ __ t __ __ __ __ __
6. __ __ __ l
7. __ u __ __ __ __ __
8. __ __ __ r

5 Complete the dialog. Use the words from Activity 4.

Captain: The wind is good. Let's put the ¹ .... up the ² ....

Sailor: We have a problem, Captain. We're too heavy. Look, the ³ .... is below the water.

Captain: That's because all our food and water is below the deck in the ⁴ ....

Sailor: Oh. How about putting them outside on the ⁵ .... ?

Captain: The boat is too heavy. I have an idea. You stand there at the front at the ⁶ .... ! I'll stand at the back at the ⁷ ....

Sailor: OK. Should I sail the boat, Captain? I'm good with the ⁸ ....

Captain: No, boy, I want you to get off the boat. I'm going to sail solo!

119

Grammar 1

> Yesterday evening at seven o'clock, my family was at home. What were we doing?

I/He/She **was**/**wasn't sailing** to the island.
You/We/They **were**/**weren't sailing** to the island.

1 Read and circle. Then match.

1 Mom **was listening** / **were listening** to the radio.
2 I **were studying** / **was studying** for a math test.
3 Dad **wasn't doing** / **weren't doing** anything – he was asleep on the couch!
4 My pet cats **was playing** / **were playing** with string.
5 My little brothers **wasn't making** / **weren't making** a noise! That was a surprise!

2 Complete the sentences. Use Past Progressive.

1 Yesterday at six o'clock, I _____ (have) dinner.
2 At two o'clock in history class, we _____ (write) a test.
3 Last night at ten o'clock, he _____ (get) ready for bed.
4 Yesterday morning at eight o'clock, they _____ (not walk) to school – it was Saturday. They _____ (sleep).
5 Last Friday at seven o'clock in the evening, she _____ (not talk) on the phone. She _____ (play) video games.
6 Yesterday at noon, you _____ (run) in a race.

3 Read and complete. Write the words in the correct form.

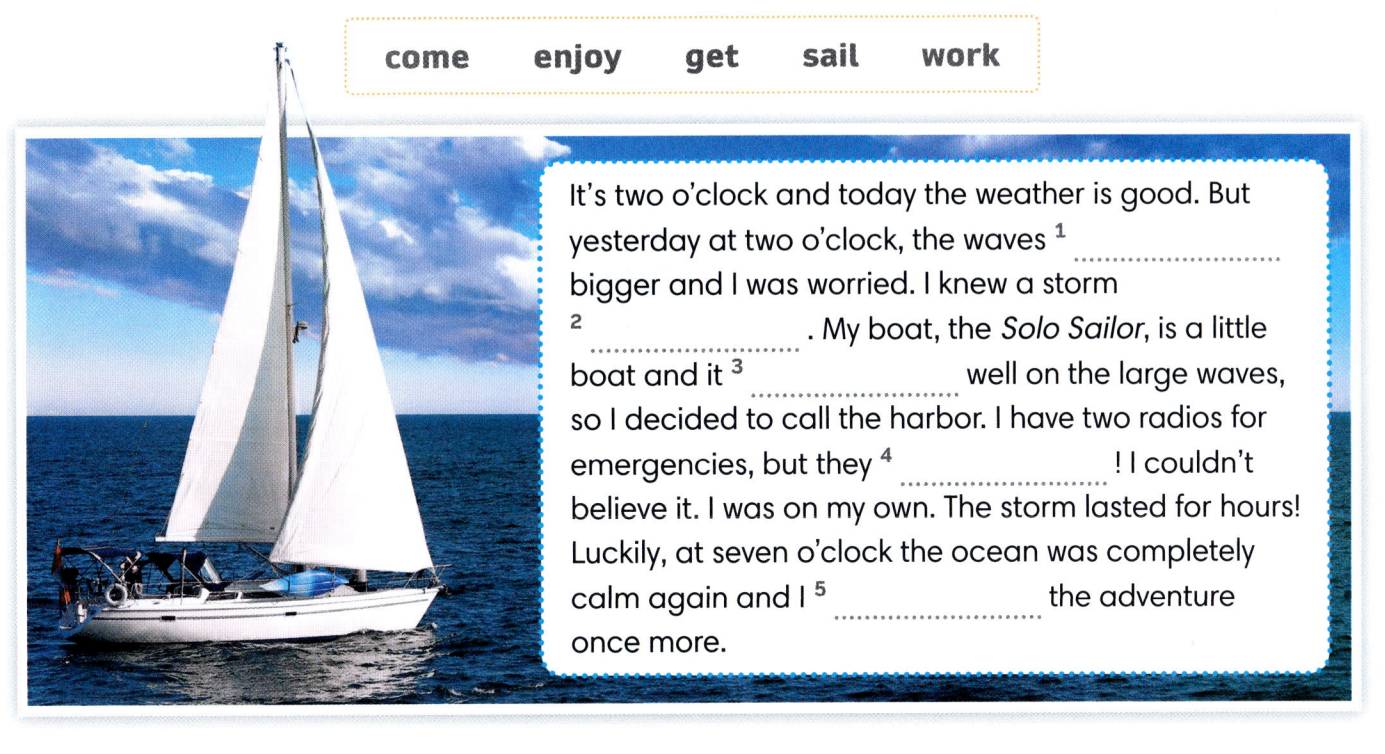

come   enjoy   get   sail   work

It's two o'clock and today the weather is good. But yesterday at two o'clock, the waves ¹ _____ bigger and I was worried. I knew a storm ² _____. My boat, the *Solo Sailor*, is a little boat and it ³ _____ well on the large waves, so I decided to call the harbor. I have two radios for emergencies, but they ⁴ _____! I couldn't believe it. I was on my own. The storm lasted for hours! Luckily, at seven o'clock the ocean was completely calm again and I ⁵ _____ the adventure once more.

4 Look at the three pictures. Write a story in 20 words or more.

Reading 2

1 Read *A Strange Sailor*. Why did Kylie and Tommy stare at the man?

....

A Strange Sailor

Tommy was standing on the beach, looking out to the ocean. It was a stormy day – the sky was dark and the waves were crashing on the beach. Suddenly, Tommy saw a strange white light out in the ocean. Then he realised it was a ship, which was rocking up and down on the waves. The Captain was standing on the deck. His face was very white and he was waving at Tommy.

Tommy realised the ship was in trouble, so he called his friend, Kylie, whose dad had a speed boat. He asked Kylie to run fast to the beach with the keys. Soon Kylie was there with the keys and a few minutes later they were speeding out to sea.

"Is there anyone else on the ship?" shouted Tommy.

"No, I was sailing alone," answered the man, climbing into their boat.

When they made it to the beach, the children noticed that he was wearing a pirate's hat and clothes, and there was a parrot clinging to his shoulder!

"What are you looking at, children? It's rude to stare!"

"Sorry," said Tommy. "Er … are you a pirate?"

"Of course, I am! I'm Paddy and this is my parrot, Victor. We were looking for our lost treasure when the storm came. Lucky for us you were standing on the beach," said the pirate. "Now, excuse us, but we have to find a new ship."

Paddy walked away and disappeared in the fog that suddenly gathered.

2 Read *A Strange Sailor* again. Read and circle.

1 At first Tommy **knows** / **doesn't know** the man on the ship.
2 Kylie is a **good** / **bad** friend because she helps Tommy.
3 Tommy is **polite** / **rude** because he apologizes.
4 Paddy is **strange** / **normal** because he's dressed as a pirate.

3 Discuss with a friend. Did Tommy and Kylie react in the right way? What would you do differently?

Vocabulary 2

1 Read, look, and label.

eye patch   nervous   rope   scar   sword

2 Write the missing consonants.

I think ¹ __i__ __o__ __ is a very interesting subject. At the moment I'm reading a book about pirates. Most of them wanted to get a ² __ u __ e amount of gold only for themselves. They were very ³ __ e __ ou __ about other pirates stealing it, so they often hid it on a remote ⁴ i __ a __ . A lot of the gold was never found and its location is still a ⁵ __ __ __ e __ __ . Some people try to find the treasure with a ⁶ __ e a __ __ e e __ o __ , but I hope it stays hidden!

3 Find and circle eight words. Then choose four and write sentences about the picture from Activity 1.

tislandgbnpoiningjmysterykophistoryychugevtjscartemropelaqsworder

123

4 Imagine you're a pirate with some treasure. What's your name? What treasure do you have? Where are you going to hide it? Think and write.

....
....
....
....

Word study: compound nouns

5 Read and match. Then complete the chart. Use a dictionary to help you.

1 sea   a island
2 treasure   b set
3 ocean   c line
4 ship   d gull
5 shore   e floor
6 fishing   f chest
7 sun   g wreck
8 desert   h net

Clue: the compound nouns that are one word all start with the same letter.

one-word compound nouns	two-word compound nouns

6 Label the pictures. Use the compound nouns from Activity 5.

124

Grammar 2

Was I/he/she/it **digging**? Yes, I/he/she/it **was**. No, I/he/she/it **wasn't**.
Were you/we/they **digging**? Yes, you/we/they **were**. No, you/we/they **weren't**.

1 Read and circle.

1 **Was** / **Were** the pirate burying treasure?
2 **Was** / **Were** the students having a history lesson?
3 Was the ship **sail** / **sailing** in a storm?
4 Were you **pulling** / **pulled** a rope?
5 Was **she** / **we** hiding behind a tree?
6 Were **he** / **they** using a metal detector?

2 Look and answer the questions from Activity 1.

125

3 Complete the dialog. Use Past Progressive.

Paul: Do you want to see my picture from the party, Grandma?

Grandma: Sure. Wow! You look scary! ¹ _____ (you/wear) a wizard costume?

Paul: No, ² _____ ! I was wearing a pirate costume!

Grandma: Oh. I can see Lucia next to you in red. ³ _____ (she/have) fun? She doesn't look happy.

Paul: Yes, ⁴ _____ . She was fine. She was trying to look scary, that's all.

Grandma: Liz and Fred look more terrifying! ⁵ _____ (they/make) scary noises?

Paul: Yes, ⁶ _____ ! They're always noisy!

4 Read and write.

1 Were you swimming in the ocean last summer?
   _____

2 Were you helping your mom with cooking yesterday?
   _____

3 Were you watching TV yesterday at 7 p.m.?
   _____

4 Was your dad wearing a tie for your birthday party?
   _____

5 Imagine you were at a party last Saturday evening. Complete the questions with one word in each blank. Then answer them.

1 What _____ you wearing at the party?
   I _____ .

2 _____ were you doing at 7 p.m.?
   I _____ .

3 What dance _____ your friends doing at 8 p.m.?
   They _____ .

4 What _____ people doing at 10 p.m.?
   They _____ .

Writing

1 Read and answer.

ELENA'S ADVENTURE

It was early morning and Elena was hiding in her dad's yacht. She loved sailing and she was looking for an adventure. Her dad was standing on deck and he was looking at the ocean. He was a brave man, with curly red hair and an eye patch. He looked like a pirate! Her dad thought he was sailing solo – he had no idea Elena was with him!

1 Where does the story take place? ....
2 Who are the main characters? ....
3 What were the main characters doing? ....
....

2 Think about your adventure story and write your ideas.

Setting .... What do they look like? ....
Characters' names ....
What are they like? What were they doing? ....
....

3 Write your story in your notebook. Use your ideas from Activity 2.

⚠ Remember

Check (✓) what your writing has.

a writing strategy:
   establish a context ☐
   introduce characters ☐

b vocabulary:
   adventure words ☐

c grammar:
   Past Progressive ☐

d correct spelling: ☐

127

Now I Know

1 Find 13 words and write them in alphabetical order.

T	C	H	A	L	L	E	N	G	E	Y
R	L	I	M	I	S	L	A	N	D	A
E	O	S	O	K	W	A	Z	E	S	C
T	N	T	O	B	A	T	T	L	E	H
R	E	O	N	T	O	W	P	S	C	T
E	L	R	L	E	S	W	O	R	D	S
A	I	Y	I	S	H	I	I	T	R	M
B	N	W	T	C	C	H	N	L	E	A
U	E	X	H	A	U	S	T	I	O	N
K	S	V	E	R	O	P	E	S	M	I
E	S	E	N	D	U	R	A	N	C	E

1 ....
2 ....
3 ....
4 ....
5 ....
6 ....
7 ....
8 ....
9 ....
10 ....
11 ....
12 ....
13 ....

2 Read and match.

1 There's a huge hole in the boat!
2 Sami wants to
3 We sailed
4 Arthur always
5 Why don't you use a metal
6 It's still a mystery where
7 This ocean is a
8 The pirate was wearing an eye

a the pirates hid their treasure.
b sails solo.
c nonstop from the U.K. to Australia.
d It's going to sink!
e navigate around the world.
f napatch over his left eye.
g detector to find the coins?
h treacherous place.

3 Read and complete with words from Activity 1.

1 I was born on this .... Its .... is fascinating.
2 Today's .... is to climb this .... as fast as you can.
3 Santiago looked scared when the pirate .... his .... at him.

128

4 Read and complete. Use the correct form of the words from the box.

> cook   have   not go   not watch   wear

1 Yesterday at seven o'clock, we _____ breakfast in the kitchen.
2 Last Sunday at eight o'clock, we _____ to school. We were at home.
3 **Abby:** _____ they _____ their boots in the rain yesterday afternoon?
   Tim: Yes, they _____ .
4 Yesterday, Fay _____ TV because she had a lot of homework.
5 At seven o'clock in the evening, Mom _____ dinner for the family.

5 Do you know what your family were doing while you were at school yesterday? Write one sentence for each family member.

1 My mom was _____ .
2 My dad _____ .
3 My _____ .
4 _____ .

Things I learn

1 Write down your three favorite new words from this unit. Which word was the most difficult?

_____

2 Write two things you found interesting about:

1 people who sail around the world   2 pirates

_____   _____

3 What qualities does a good adventure story have?

_____

129

10 Why do we raise money for charity?

1 Name two different ways people can raise money for charity. What would you like to learn about charities?

....

....

2 Circle the words related to charities. What else do you think you will learn about raising money for charity?

backyard   food bank   help   island   volunteer   water   zoo

....

3 Watch the video. Read and complete.

| bin | food | fresh | meals | over | packaging | perfect | together |

Bristol FareShare is a charity that gives ¹..................... to people. They send it to other charities that prepare ².................... . They collect food that was going to be thrown in the ³..................... . All the food at the factory is ⁴....................., but there might be a problem with the ⁵..................... or it might not look ⁶....................., but is still edible. ⁷..................... 70 volunteers work at the charity. They work ⁸..................... to help people who need it, like the homeless and refugees.

4 Read and match.

1 A person who doesn't have anywhere to live is   **a** factory.
2 Something that you can eat is   **b** enthusiasm.
3 When you're excited about something you show   **c** refugee.
4 A person who has to leave their country to stay safe is a   **d** homeless.
5 A large building where people make things is a   **e** edible.

Reading 1

1 Read *Martindale Primary School blog*. Think about the underlined words and phrases and circle the correct meaning.

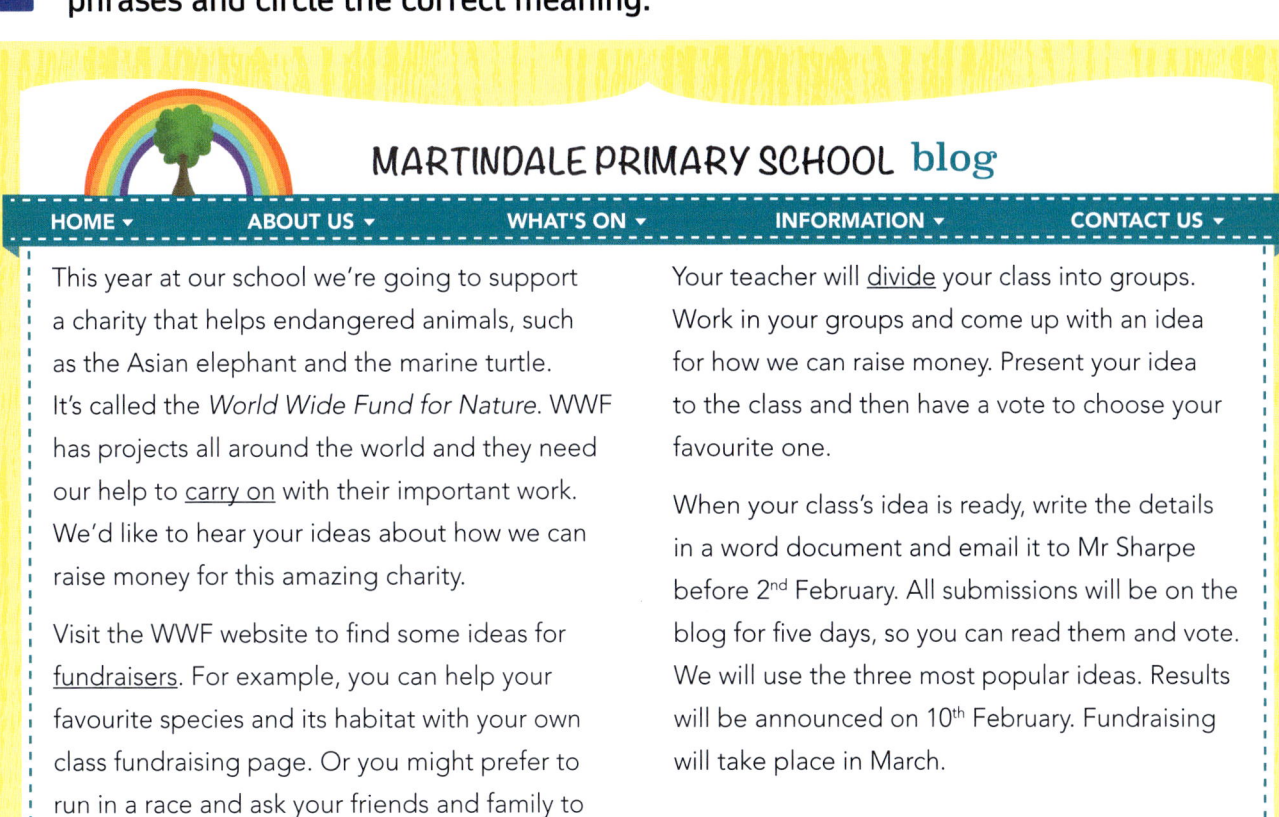

MARTINDALE PRIMARY SCHOOL blog

HOME ▾ | ABOUT US ▾ | WHAT'S ON ▾ | INFORMATION ▾ | CONTACT US ▾

This year at our school we're going to support a charity that helps endangered animals, such as the Asian elephant and the marine turtle. It's called the *World Wide Fund for Nature*. WWF has projects all around the world and they need our help to <u>carry on</u> with their important work. We'd like to hear your ideas about how we can raise money for this amazing charity.

Visit the WWF website to find some ideas for <u>fundraisers</u>. For example, you can help your favourite species and its habitat with your own class fundraising page. Or you might prefer to run in a race and ask your friends and family to sponsor you to <u>participate</u>.

Your teacher will <u>divide</u> your class into groups. Work in your groups and come up with an idea for how we can raise money. Present your idea to the class and then have a vote to choose your favourite one.

When your class's idea is ready, write the details in a word document and email it to Mr Sharpe before 2nd February. All submissions will be on the blog for five days, so you can read them and vote. We will use the three most popular ideas. Results will be announced on 10th February. Fundraising will take place in March.

1 carry on — **stop** / **continue**
2 fundraisers — events organized to **spend** / **collect** money
3 participate — **be a part of** / **watch** something
4 divide — put into **smaller groups** / **one big group**

2 Read *Martindale Primary School blog* again. Find the words or phrases that match these meanings.

Paragraph 1 at risk of going extinct: ....

Paragraph 2 like more: ....

Paragraph 3 make a choice: ....

Paragraph 4 happen: ....

3 Work with a friend. Think of a fundraising idea for Martindale Primary School.

131

Vocabulary 1

1 Complete the crossword.

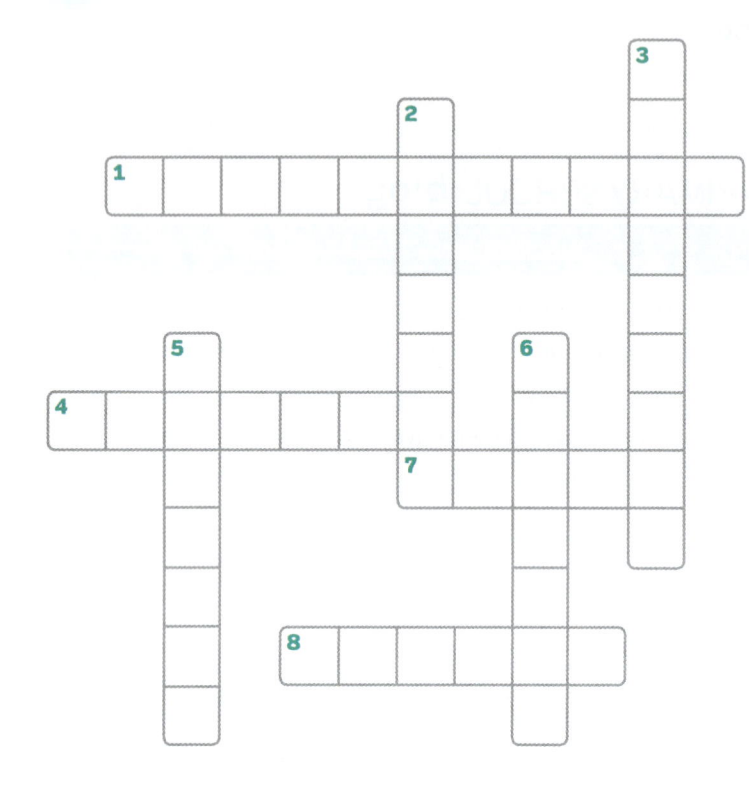

Across

1. You write this on your phone and send it to someone else's phone.
4. Another word for help.
7. This is a letter that you send through the internet.
8. Give something to a person or organization for free.

Down

2. It's a place on the internet where you can find information.
3. This means you often do something at the same time of the day or week.
5. Give money to charity if someone walks or runs a particular distance.
6. It's an organization that helps people or animals.

2 Read and complete. There are two extra words.

| donate | email | raise | regularly | sponsor | volunteer |

1. Miray wants to run a ten kilometer race for charity. Can you _____ her?
2. Our class hopes to _____ money for WWF. We're going to have a cake sale.
3. Isa and Nick _____ at the animal center. They help there in their free time.
4. Some people _____ money to charity every month from their bank accounts.

3 What charities do you know? What can you do to support them?

....

....

....

132

Vocabulary challenge: different personalities

4 Read and look. Label the pictures with the words in bold.

1. Neil is a **polite** boy. He always says thank you.
2. Robin is **dishonest**. She steals from other people!
3. Maia is always **miserable**. She cries all the time!
4. Lee is **greedy**. He loves money and he doesn't share it.
5. Jada is a **caring** girl. She always helps people and animals.
6. Coach Jones is **enthusiastic**. He gives his team a lot of support.

5 Which personalities are good for volunteers and which ones are bad? Complete the chart with the words from Activity 4. Then add words of your own.

Good	Bad

Grammar 1

> I/You/We **know/understand how to** help.
> I/You/We **don't know/understand how to** help.
>
> He/She **knows/understands how to** help.
> He/She **doesn't know/understand how to** help.
>
> **Do** you **know/understand how to** help?
> **Does** he/she **know/understand how to** help?

1 Read and match. Then check (✔) the sentences that are true for you.

1 I know how to
2 I don't understand
3 I know how to play
4 I understand how a
5 I don't know how to say

a computer works.
b soccer.
c bake cookies.
d where I live in English.
e how charities work.

2 🎧 05 📋 Listen and draw lines.

Javier   Chris   Jackie   Ethan   Sarah   Rick

134

3 Complete the sentences. Use the correct form of the words in parentheses.

1 My dad .... (understand/play) cards.
2 I .... (not know/make) an omelet.
3 We .... (know/raise) money for a charity.
4 Grandpa .... (not understand/create) a blog.
5 .... (you know/send) a picture by email?
6 .... (Mom know/set) a new password?

4 Write the words in order.

1 I / how / an / email / know / send / to

....

2 upload / how / to / Dave / pictures / understands

....

3 play / understand / how / you / to / chess / don't

....

4 doesn't / Alexis / know / to / a / drive / car / how

....

5 does / message / how / know / send / a / text / Grandma / to

.... ?

5 Write sentences that are true for you and your family.

bake cookies   buy things online   fix a car   make party hats
ride a skateboard   use a cell phone

1 ....
2 ....
3 ....
4 ....
5 ....
6 ....

Reading 2

Sahil's Story

Sahil woke up very early every day. He had to make breakfast for the family, sweep the house, then head out to the garbage dump before eight o'clock. He spent all day at the garbage dump, looking for things he and his family could use or sell. Sahil was only nine years old, but his family was poor, and he had to help bring in some money. His dad worked in another country far away, so Sahil had to help his mom and three sisters. But Sahil had a dream.

"What do you want to be when you grow up?" an older boy asked him one day.

"I want to be a teacher," Sahil said and the boy laughed.

One morning, a woman came to Sahil's house. She talked to Sahil's mom.

Me at school

"That woman was a volunteer from a charity that helped poor children. A school in Canada wants to sponsor you and your sisters, so you can go to school," Sahil's mom said, smiling. Sahil's school life started the following week.

At first, he sat very quietly at his desk. But soon he made friends and he learned to read and write. He was a very good student and he did well in all his subjects. Sahil knew that one day his dream could come true. All he had to do was study hard.

1 Read *Sahil's Story*. Write two similarities and two differences between you and Sahil.

Similarities: ....

Differences: ....

2 Read *Sahil's Story* again and answer the questions.

1 Why did Sahil have to work? ....
2 How many children were in Sahil's family? ....
3 What did Sahil learn at school? ....
4 What does Sahil have to do to become a teacher? ....

3 Why is it important to help poor children to go to school?

....

....

Vocabulary 2

1 Write the letters in order. Then match the words to their definitions.

1 r y j r e a n c   ....   a very often
2 s o n n t a c t   ....   b useful or willing to help
3 f u e q t n r e l y .... c metal container for storing water or gas
4 e h u l l p f   ....   d take care of
5 a c r e   o r f   ....   e a deep hole in the ground with water in it
6 l e l w   ....   f happening all the time

2 Read and circle.

Red Nose Day

Comic Relief is a charity in the U.K. It's a(n) ¹ **organization / well / collect** that wants to ² **helpful / improve / contribute** the lives of poor people around the world. Once a year on Red Nose Day, TV stars host a hilarious show, so the charity can ³ **improve / generous / collect** donations from viewers. People all over the U.K. wear red noses to show their support for the charity. People are always ⁴ **frequently / generous / constant** and the charity raises millions of pounds every year.

3 Complete with the words from Activity 1.

Peter's grandparents live on a ranch, but they're very old and the work is a ¹ .... worry for them. Peter and his parents ² .... visit and when they're there everyone's very ³ .... Peter especially likes to help ⁴ .... the animals. He feeds them and brings them water from the ⁵ .... in a ⁶ ....

137

4 Circle the odd one out. Then write one sentence with each word you circled.

1 improve   well   collect   care for
2 helpful   generous   improve   constant
3 frequently   well   jerry can   organization

....

....

....

Word study: phrasal verbs with *for*

5 Read and match.

1 Diego, there's a package **waiting for** you in the kitchen.
2 My dad loves baseball, he always **roots for** his favorite team.
3 I can't believe Hassan **fell for** your trick. It's so silly!
4 What does U.S.A. **stand for**?
5 I think I can **speak for** the entire class; we're sorry about our behavior.

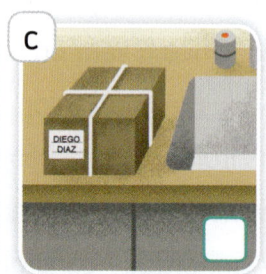

a   b   c   d   e

6 Read and complete. Use the phrasal verbs in bold from Activity 5.

1 **Betty:** We don't want pizza for dinner.
   Sam: .... yourself. I'd love pizza for dinner.
2 Minnie! Ella is .... you outside. Hurry up!
3 Your team always loses. Why do you still .... them?
4 **Eva:** Please tell me you didn't believe Tim's trick.
   Anna: I knew he was up to something, but I still .... it.
5 Look at this message. What do these pictures .... ?

138

Grammar 2

I/He/She **was looking** on the internet when I/he/she **found** the picture.
You/We/They **were looking** on the internet when you/we/they **found** it.

1 Read and circle.

Dear diary,
Today I ¹ **was playing** / **played** on my computer when Tommy ² **was running** / **ran** into my room. We ³ **talked** / **were talking** when Mom ⁴ **walked** / **was walking** in. She ⁵ **was getting** / **got angry** about the mess in my room when Dad ⁶ **was coming** / **came** in looking for his charger. I ⁷ **tried** / **was trying** to talk to everyone when Grandma ⁸ **video-called** / **was video-calling**. They ⁹ **were talking** / **talked** at the same time so I ¹⁰ **covered** / **was covering** my ears. At that moment they shouted "Happy April Fool's Day!"
I couldn't believe I fell for it!

2 Complete the dialog. Use Past Progressive or Past Simple.

Paul: Last weekend when I ¹ _____ (play) video games, my computer crashed!

Maria: Oh, no! What did you do?

Paul: I asked my brother to fix it. But he was listening to music when I ² _____ (ask) him and he told me to go away!

Maria: Oh, no!

Paul: It's OK. He ³ _____ (fix) it for me yesterday. Dad helped him.

Maria: Is it OK now?

Paul: Yes. But while they ⁴ _____ (work) Mom told me to finish my school assignment. So while I was doing homework, my brother ⁵ _____ (turn) on my computer and started playing my favorite game!

3 Complete the sentences. Use Past Progressive or Past Simple and the correct verbs.

1

take   visit

Pam .... the zoo when a monkey .... her cap.

3

do   start

We .... a sponsored walk when it .... to rain.

5

call   write

Dad .... an email when his boss .... him.

2

bake   steal

I .... cookies with Mom when my dog .... the butter!

4

collect   see

The girls .... a snake when they .... water.

6

fall asleep   watch

While we .... TV, Grandpa ....

4 Write four true sentences about things that happened to you. Use *while* and *when*.

1 Yesterday I was ....
2 While ....
3 ....
4 ....

140

Writing

1 Read and circle.

Sponsored ART!

Are you interested in helping a charity?

Do you know **¹ how / why** to draw or paint?

If you do, volunteer at our Sponsored Art event and help us **² raise / improve** money for *Schools for All*! Please come and buy our pictures or **³ volunteer / donate** some pictures for this important **⁴ charity / well**. We need your **⁵ organization / support**!

WHEN: 10:00 A.M., SATURDAY, JANUARY 15TH
WHERE: JACOBS ELEMENTARY SCHOOL HALL
WHO: STUDENTS AND FAMILIES ARE WELCOME!

2 Think about the charity event you chose and answer the questions.

1 What's the name of your event?

2 What do volunteers need to know?

3 When and where is the event?

4 Who's welcome?

3 Write your notice in your notebook. Use your ideas from Activity 2.

(!) Remember

Check (✓) what your writing has.

a writing strategy:
when ☐
where ☐
who ☐

b vocabulary:
charity words ☐

c grammar:
know how ☐

d correct spelling: ☐

141

Now I Know

1 Find and circle 10 words or phrases. Then complete the chart.

careforcharitysponsororganizationimprovedonatejerrycancollectwebsitetextmessage

Nouns	Verbs

2 Read and circle.

1   a   We give local charities a lot of **support** / **well**.
    b   The villagers walk a long way to collect water from the **support** / **well**.

2   a   This charity needs people to **care for** / **volunteer** to help.
    b   It's important to **volunteer** / **care for** elderly family members.

3   a   How to help the poor is a **constant** / **generous** problem for charities.
    b   Thank you for your **constant** / **generous** donation.

4   a   Please help me **sponsor** / **raise** money for WWF.
    b   Please **raise** / **sponsor** me on this walk for charity.

5   a   We **regularly** / **helpful** donate money to charity.
    b   Thank you for being so **regularly** / **helpful** at the event.

3 Complete the sentences. Use the correct form of the verbs from the box. There's one extra word.

> call   go   play   sleep   study

1   Yesterday I _____ when a loud noise woke me up.
2   The dogs _____ with a ball when it fell in the lake.
3   We _____ for a test when Mom came home from work.
4   Fay was listening to music when I _____ into her room.

142

4 Look and write sentences. Use (*not*) *know how* or (*not*) *understand how*.

1 Dan / ride a mountain bike

....

2 May and Jane / ski down the mountain

....

3 Uncle Tom / do this puzzle

....

4 Grandma and her friend / pay at this checkout

....

Things I learn

1 Write down your three favorite new words from this unit. Which word was the most difficult?

....

2 Write two things you found interesting about:

1 charities that help people and animals

2 organizing charity events

....

....

3 How can you find out more about charities?

....

11 How are we similar but different?

1 What words do you use to describe your best friend? What would you like to learn about making friends?

....

....

2 Circle the words that could be used to describe people. What do you think you will learn about similar and different qualities in people?

friendly   furry   green   lazy   treacherous   young

....

3 Watch the video and complete the sentences.

> create   fall   give   know   make   stress

1 Good friends .... you support when you're feeling sad.
2 It's OK if they sometimes .... you out.
3 You can .... memories with good friends.
4 Good friends .... when to listen and when to talk.
5 If you want to .... friends, try not to be shy.
6 Even good friends sometimes .... out.

4 Complete the chart.

adjective	verb
1 trustworthy	
2 reliable	
3 inclusive	

5 Complete the sentences with the verbs from Activity 4.

1 My friends .... me in activities and conversations. I never feel left out.
2 My best friend is always there for me. I can .... on him.
3 I can .... my friend, I know she can keep my secrets.

Reading 1

1 Read *Anne Arrives in Avonlea*. Circle the adjectives that describe Anne in red and the adjectives that describe Matthew in green.

happy   kind   little   quiet   red-haired   shy   surprised   talkative

CHAPTER 1
Anne Arrives in Avonlea

Matthew Cuthbert drove to the station. There was only one person there, a little girl about eleven years old. She was thin, with large, gray eyes and long, red hair. She wore a short, ugly dress and carried an old bag.

When she saw Matthew, she smiled and put out her hand. "Hello, I'm Anne!" she said. "I'm from the orphanage."

Matthew was surprised to see her because he was expecting a boy. He was quiet and rather shy, so he wasn't sure how to tell her there's been a mistake.

"I'm very happy to see you. If you didn't come, I was going to sleep in that tree over there and then wait again for you tomorrow," she said brightly.

"Sorry I was late," he said. "Come on. I'll take you home."

"I'm very glad you came because I didn't really want to sleep in a tree all night. I'm sure sleeping in a tree is exciting, but driving is exciting too, isn't it? This is much more fun than the orphanage, and I'm very happy that I'm going to have a family. I didn't have anyone at the orphanage and it wasn't a nice place. Maybe I'm a bad child to talk like that, but the orphanage was horrible and now I'm much happier because I'm with you. I hope you don't mind me talking so much."

"I don't mind. You can talk as much as you like," said Matthew.

2 Read *Anne Arrives in Avonlea* again. Complete the sentences.

1 Anne is .... years old.
2 Her bag is ....
3 Anne says the orphanage was ....
4 Matthew .... Anne talking.

3 💬 Why didn't Matthew tell Anne that there was a mistake? Was it the right thing to do? Discuss with a friend.

Vocabulary 1

1 Find seven more words. Write them next to their opposite meanings.

T	H	O	U	G	H	T	F	U	L
A	R	P	C	P	O	T	I	V	A
L	U	E	F	U	T	N	Y	T	E
K	U	N	W	I	E	E	E	M	H
A	B	O	P	E	S	A	T	E	O
T	V	S	R	O	T	G	H	A	N
I	S	T	U	B	B	O	R	N	E
V	T	U	D	E	T	A	L	Q	S
E	A	R	R	O	G	A	N	T	T

1 not caring about others: *thoughtful*
2 changing their mind easily: ....
3 not promise: ....
4 never speaking: ....
5 private and shy: ....
6 saying nice things: ....
7 telling lies: ....
8 modest: ....

2 What qualities do you look for in a friend? Number these qualities 1–5 in order of importance (1 = most important).

talkative ☐
honest ☐
open ☐
imaginative ☐
thoughtful ☐

3 Read and complete.

> feeling   open
> something in common
> stubborn   think

My best friend

This is Rex and he's my best friend. I'm a boy and he's a dog, but we actually have ¹............................ – we both love playing at the park! Sometimes Rex can be ²............................ when he doesn't want to go home after we play. I have to pull him! I always know what he wants because he's ³............................ . Animals don't hide their feelings, you see. He understands me, too. When I'm ⁴............................ sad, he sits next to me with his head on my knees. I ⁵............................ Rex is the best dog in the world.

146

4. What do you have in common with the person next to you?

....

....

Vocabulary challenge: people you know

5 Read and circle the words for people.

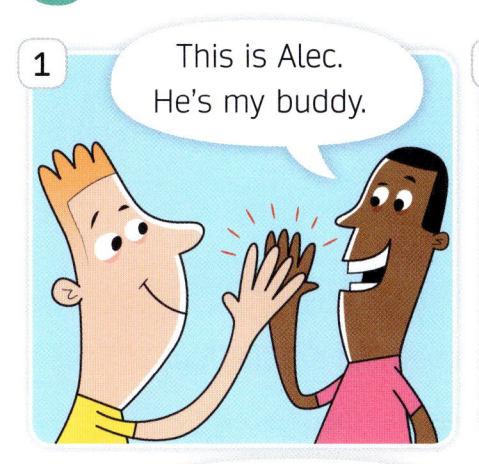

1. This is Alec. He's my buddy.
2. Walter is my neighbor. He lives at number 21.
3. I go to a big school and I have a lot of schoolmates.
4. We're robbing a bank! Ted is my accomplice!
5. Jen and I are in the same soccer team. We're teammates.
6. We love the waltz. Claire is my partner.

6 Read and write. Use the words you circled from Activity 5.

1 a person who helps another commit a crime

2 someone you dance with

3 a good friend

4 people on the same sports team

5 a person who lives next door

6 students in your school

147

Grammar 1

He's so rich he can buy **anything** he wants.
Is there **anyone** in your family who has red hair?
Do you want to buy **something** from the supermarket?
I went to the park, but there wasn't **anybody** there.
Let's find **someone** who can help us.
I knew **nothing** about today's meeting.
She knocked on the door, but **no one** answered.
I felt that **everything** was going wrong.
Everyone had fun at the party last night.

People
somebody/someone
everybody/everyone
nobody/no one
anybody/anyone

Things
something
everything
nothing
anything

1 Read and match.

1 Where's the bank?
2 What do you want to eat?
3 Who knocked at the window?
4 Happy birthday!
5 Can we start the meeting?

a Thanks. Let's do something special today.
b I don't know. Let's ask someone.
c Yes. Everyone's here.
d Nobody. It was the tree on the glass.
e I'm not sure. There's nothing nice on the menu.

2 Read, choose, and write.

MAKING FRIENDS AT A NEW SCHOOL

Imagine you start at a new school and you don't know **1** .... How does that feel? It's lonely, isn't it? Most kids in this situation try to find **2** .... to talk to. But for shy kids, there's **3** .... worse than trying to talk to people you don't know. They don't know how to start a conversation because they can't think of **4** .... interesting to talk about. Teachers can help by organizing a group activity to help students get to know each other. This can give a shy student **5** .... to talk about. It isn't the answer to **6** .... 's problems, but it's a start.

1	nobody	anybody	somebody	4	anything	no one	something
2	something	anything	someone	5	anything	something	nothing
3	anything	nothing	everything	6	nothing	everyone	everything

3 Read and complete.

| anybody | anything | everybody | everything | nobody |
| nothing | somebody | something | | |

1. I know _____ who works here. His name is Mark.
2. Thanks to _____ for coming to my party. I'm happy to see you.
3. I called the store, but _____ answered. I'll try again later.
4. Hello? Is _____ there?
5. I want to tell you _____. It's a secret.
6. Doug is really smart. He knows _____ about computers.
7. We need to go shopping. There's _____ in the fridge.
8. I just moved here so I don't know _____ about the town.

4 Read and complete.

My name's Christine and this is my best friend, Jess. We do [1] e_____ together. I tell Jess my secrets. I can tell her [2] a_____. We have a lot in common and we always find [3] s_____ fun to do on the weekend. [4] N_____ understands me like Jess does and she's [5] s_____ I can rely on. I think we'll be friends forever.

5 Circle the odd one out. Then write one sentence with each word you circled.

1	somebody	everybody	anything
2	no one	anybody	anyone
3	everything	nothing	nobody

_____
_____
_____

149

Reading 2

Twins

I'm Rodrigo and this is my brother, Santi. People say we look like each other. We've got black hair and dark eyes. We've got small noses and round faces. We're quite like each other too. We're both quite shy and quiet. And we've got a lot in common – we both like listening to music and playing football – I suppose that's because we grew up together and did the same things as children. It's also because we're twins!

How common are twins?
Twins are more common nowadays than 30 years ago. About three percent of all births are twins. One reason is that couples go to the doctor for IVF treatment. This is a medical treatment that helps a woman get pregnant – and it often creates more than one baby. Also many mums are older these days, and older women are more likely to have twins.

Identical twins
Maternal twins come from one of their mother's eggs. The egg divides in two and two babies start to grow. When they're born they don't always look the same, but as they grow, they start to look more alike, so it can be hard to tell who is who. Identical twins are always the same gender.

Non-identical twins
Fraternal twins form from two separate eggs inside their mother. They look like each other because they're siblings, but they aren't exactly the same, so people can easily tell who is who. Fraternal twins can be different genders.

1 Read *Twins*. What's the main purpose of this text?

....

2 Read *Twins* again. Complete the sentences with one word.

1 About .... of babies born are twins.
2 An .... mom is more likely to have twins.
3 Identical twins start out as .... egg.
4 Non-identical twins start out as .... eggs.

3 Do you know any twins? What do they look like? What are their personalities like?

Vocabulary 2

1 Read and circle.

1. Your genes **determine** / **respond** / **disagree** the color of your eyes.
2. Alp **behaved** / **responded** / **disagreed** happily to the news about the vacation.
3. We **behaved** / **determined** / **disagreed** about what to do that weekend.
4. Parents should teach their children how to **determine** / **behave** / **disagree** in public.

2 Read and write **T** (true) or **F** (false).

1. Someone who is forgetful remembers things very well. ....
2. Brothers and sisters always behave the same way. ....
3. People who disagree have the same opinion. ....
4. Every person in the world is unique. ....
5. Your genes and your environment determine your character. ....
6. Active people do a lot of things. ....

3 Read and complete. Then match.

> forgetful   positive   practical   similar   unique

1. Dad didn't remember Mom's birthday! He's so _____.
2. Mom is _____. She keeps the cooking spoons by the cooker.
3. Trish and Sandy are very _____ – I never know who is who.
4. We're similar in some aspects, but in the end everyone is _____.
5. I try to stay _____ when I make a mistake.

a   b

4 Think and write.

1 Can you say that you're practical? Why/Why not?

....

2 Is anyone you know forgetful? What do they usually forget?

....

3 Is your character similar to anyone in your family? Who?

....

Word study: prefix *dis-* for opposites of adjectives/verbs

5 Write the opposite of these words in the chart. Use the prefix *dis-*.

agree   approve
honest   like
loyal   organized
respect   similar

Verbs	Adjectives

6 Complete the sentences with the words from Activity 5. Use a dictionary to help.

Verbs

1 My parents don't like jeans with holes. They .... of untidy clothes.
2 I like swimming, but I .... pools, so I always swim in the ocean.
3 You should be polite to older people. They know a lot more about life, so you shouldn't .... them.
4 I don't think you're right. In fact, I completely .... with your opinion.

Adjectives

5 You can never find anything because you're so ....! You should clean up.
6 Dean and Sam are brothers. They aren't ...., but they don't look exactly the same.
7 He's a .... person so he will never support you when you need help.
8 Danny never tells the truth. He's so .... that he lies about everything.

Grammar 2

Who **do you look like**?
I look like my dad. We both have blond hair.

Who **does he/she look like**?
He/She looks like his/her dad. They both have blue eyes.

Who **are you like**?
I'm like my mom. We're both pretty stubborn.

Who **is he/she like**?
He's/She's like her mom. They're both shy.

1 Read and check (✔) the correct picture.

Hi! I'm Pete. People say I look a lot like my dad because of our red hair. I look a bit like Grandpa, too, but my hair is curly. Maybe when I get old I will look like him more! Dad looks like Grandpa because they both have short hair and green eyes, but Grandpa's hair is gray now.
I'm also a lot like my dad – we're both active. We play soccer, baseball, and tennis. Grandpa isn't like us at all – he prefers to sit down and watch.

2 Read and circle.

1 **Ray:** **Is Dave like** / **Does Dave look like** his brother?
  Esther: Yes, they're both very practical.

2 **We're like** / **We look like** each other. We have brown eyes, brown hair, and we're tall.

3 Mom **is like** / **looks like** her sister. They love the same things and have the same hobbies.

4 My friends **are like** / **look like** me a lot. We're all talkative and funny.

5 I **am like** / **look like** my brother. We both have round faces and black hair.

6 **Nate:** Who **are you like** / **do you look like** in your family?
  Lucy: My mom. We have similar noses.

3 Look at the pictures of Steve and Emma's family. Then complete the sentences. Use *be like* and *look like* and the words from the box.

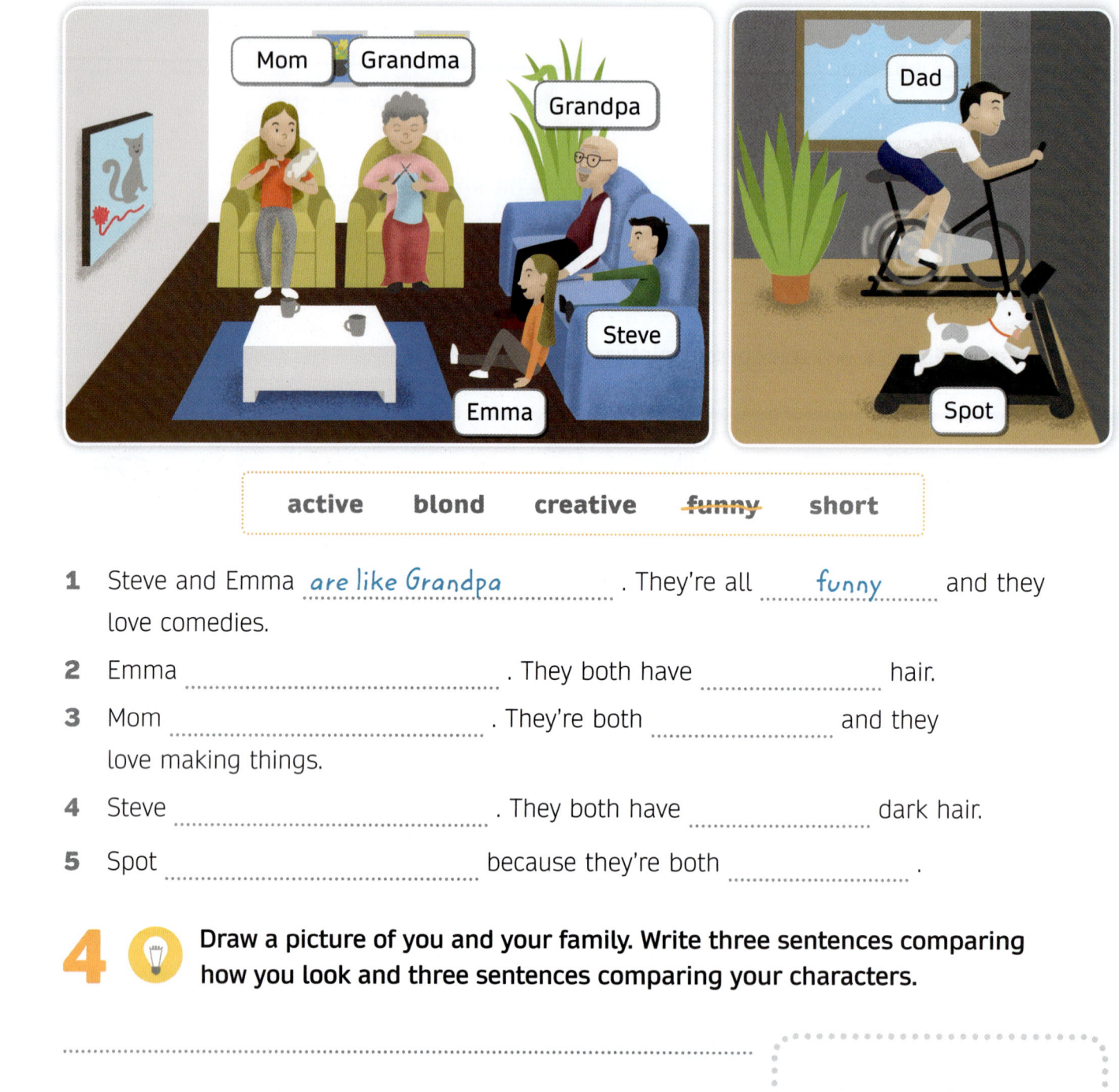

---

active   blond   creative   ~~funny~~   short

---

1. Steve and Emma <u>are like Grandpa</u>. They're all <u>funny</u> and they love comedies.
2. Emma _____. They both have _____ hair.
3. Mom _____. They're both _____ and they love making things.
4. Steve _____. They both have _____ dark hair.
5. Spot _____ because they're both _____.

4 Draw a picture of you and your family. Write three sentences comparing how you look and three sentences comparing your characters.

154

Writing

1 Read and complete.

> active   brown   curly   positive   short   similar   tall

Me and My Best Friend

I'm Tony and I'm twelve years old. My best friend, Gabe, is eleven. I think we're good friends because we're ¹................... . We look a bit like each other – we both have ²..................., ³................... hair, and ⁴................... eyes. We're also both ⁵................... . I think we're like each other in character, too – we're both ⁶................... and ⁷................... . We also have a lot in common – we both like to play basketball and we like the same video games.

2 Think about one of your friends. Complete the information.

1 Name and age: ....

2 Appearance: ....

3 Personality: ....

4 Hobbies: ....

5 Things we have in common: ....

3 Write a description of your friend in your notebook. Use your ideas from Activity 2.

! Remember

Check (✓) what your writing has.

a writing strategy:
a variety of adjectives ☐

b vocabulary:
words describing appearance ☐
words describing personality ☐

c grammar:
be like ☐
look like ☐

d correct spelling: ☐

155

Now I Know

1 Read and circle.

1 I have to ask **somebody** / **something** to help me.
2 Do you want **anything** / **anybody** to drink?
3 Hi **everything** / **everybody**! How are you?
4 The store was closed. **Anything** / **Nobody** was there.
5 I think friendship is **something** / **anyone** very important.
6 I have **no one** / **nothing** to say about the subject.
7 **Somebody** / **Everything** you need for a picnic is in the kitchen.
8 I didn't meet **anything** / **anyone** at the mall. I went on my own.

2 Read and complete. Then match.

| forgetful | honest | imaginative | mean | stubborn | talkative | unique |

1 Please stop talking!
2 Is Anika writing another story?
3 Where are my keys?
4 No, I won't try again. I don't want to.
5 Excuse me, is this your wallet?
6 Your dress looks ugly!
7 No two people are the same.

a Did you lose them again? You're so ....!
b Oh, yes. Thank you for being so ....
c Yes. She's very ....
d You don't have to be .... about it!
e Sorry! I'm too .... sometimes!
f That's true. We're all ....
g Please don't be .... It's easy.

3 Read and complete. Use *be like* or *look like*.

I have two schoolmates who ¹ .... each other a lot. They have long hair, dark eyes, and they're short. I know a lot of people have dark eyes, but Yuki and Mei ² .... sisters! Yuki thinks it's funny and she often wears similar clothes as Mei. It makes them ³ .... twins even more! They spend a lot of time together because they ⁴ .... each other in many ways. They're both active and play a lot of baseball. Mei was shy when she was younger, but now she ⁵ .... Yuki – open and talkative.

156

4 Write the letters in order. Then use the words to complete the dialog.

d i g r e s a e .... p o e n d r s .... b e h e v a ....
m e t i n d e r e .... e e l n i f g .... k h t i n ....

Isa: We're cousins but we don't look like each other much. Do you ¹ .... that's the same for other cousins?

Ian: No. Our genes ² .... the color of our hair and eyes, so people from the same family often look similar. You look a lot like Grandma, for example.

Isa: But we don't ³ .... the same way to different situations. I'm more open.

Ian: I ⁴ .... Grandma is open too, but she's older and kinder.

Isa: Ha ha! It's true. When I'm ⁵ .... upset, I can be rude!

Ian: So can I! We don't look like each other, but we often ⁶ .... the same!

5 Describe one of your family members. What do they look like? What are they like?

....
....
....

Things I learn

1 Write down your three favorite new words from this unit. Which word was the most difficult?

....

2 Write two things you found interesting about:

1 things that determine our personality

....

2 things that influence the way we look

....

3 What qualities does a good friend have?

....

12 How did people live in the past?

1 In the past, children had to work. What jobs do you think they did? What would you like to learn about that?

....

....

2 Circle the things you think people had 150 years ago. What do you think you will learn about life in the past?

bread   brick houses   computers   electricity   newspapers   tables

....

3 🎬 12-1 BBC Watch the video. Read and write **T** (true) or **F** (false).

1. In Victorian schools boys and girls could sit together. ....
2. People thought education was more important for boys than for girls. ....
3. Girls had extra lessons in math, technology, and drawing. ....
4. Some people thought that education for girls was a waste of money. ....
5. There weren't lots of job opportunities for girls. ....

4 Read and complete.

> apart   discipline   idle   practical   prosper

1. The opposite of keep together is keep ....
2. Lessons that teach you to sew and mend are .... lessons.
3. Good behavior means the same as good ....
4. A saying from Victorian times was " .... people never ...." It means that if you're lazy you won't be successful.

158

Reading 1

The Daily News *May 29, 1879*

Electric Light!

Mr. Thomas Edison did his first test of a light bulb on October 22nd and the bulb burned for 13.5 hours. When he showed his invention to the public, he said "We will make electricity so cheap that only the rich will burn candles." We asked a local factory owner, Mr. Charles Townsend, what he thinks of electric light.

"I believe Mr. Edison's invention is going to become very popular, and soon light bulbs will be present in people's homes and at their places of work. It will completely change the way we live."

The Daily News *March 7, 1876*

Going Underground!

On January 10th, 1863, the Metropolitan Railway opened its first underground railway line under the City of London. On the first day, 38,000 passengers took the train. We asked two people what they think.

"I live in the suburbs outside London, and I can get all the way to work on the train in less than an hour. It's brilliant," said Mr. James Foy.

"I took the underground train, but the smoke and dirt made me sick. I'd rather walk or ride my bike. I think the railway will fail," predicts Mr. Arthur Peeps.

The Daily News *August 2, 1826*

A View from the Window

A few months ago, a French inventor called Monsieur Nicéphore Niépce created a permanent image on paper with a machine called a camera obscura. The image was taken from a window and it shows two men working.

"This is going to change the world of images. Until today, talented people painted or drew. Now we can use a machine to take "photographs." I think the "photographic camera" will one day become quite popular, but it will be expensive," said Mrs. Francis Davis, an artist.

---

1 Read *The Daily News* and complete the sentences.

1 Thomas Edison predicted that electric light would be _____ enough for everyone.
2 Mr. Townsend predicted that there would be _____ in everyone's homes.
3 Arthur Peeps predicted that the underground railway would _____ .
4 Mrs. Davis predicted that cameras would be popular, but _____ .

2 Which of the predictions in Activity 1 were correct? Which were not?

....
....

Vocabulary 1

1 Complete the crossword and find the hidden word. What does it mean?

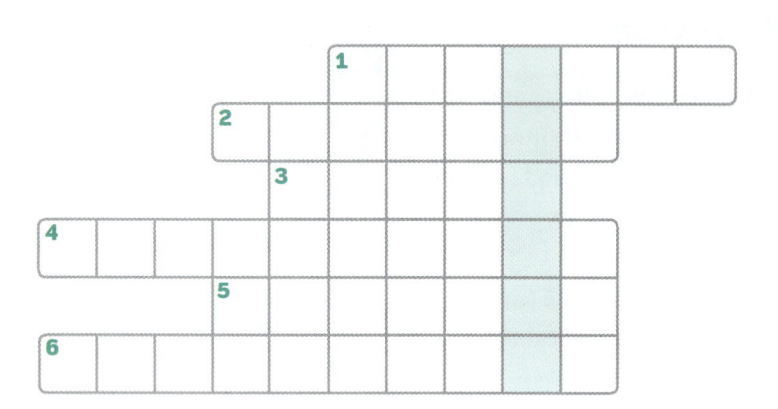

The hidden word is .... It means ....

2 Complete the sentences.

1 When my grandpa was young, he often traveled by h_ _ _ _ and c_ _ _ .
2 The area on the edge of a city is called a s_ _ _ _ b.
3 In the U.K., the s_ _ _ _ y is called the underground.
4 Before supermarkets, you had to buy bread from the b_ _ _ r.
5 A lot of people c_ _ _ _ _ e to work on a bus or train.

3 Circle the odd one out. Then write sentences with the words you circled.

1 baker   locomotive   butcher
2 marvel   subway   railway
3 subway   commute   horse and cart

....

....

....

Vocabulary challenge: inventions that changed the world

4 Decode the words. Which of the inventions do you use in your everyday life?

A	B	C	D	E	F	G	H	I	J	K	L	M	N	O	P	Q	R	S	T	U	V	W	X	Y	Z
1	2	3	4	5	6	7	8	9	10	11	12	13	14	15	16	17	18	19	20	21	22	23	24	25	26

1 W H E E L
   23 8 5 5 12

2 C O M P A S S
   3 15 13 16 1 19 19

3 P R I N T I N G   P R E S S
   16 18 9 14 20 9 14 7   16 18 5 19 19

4 E N G I N E
   5 14 7 9 14 5

5 T E L E P H O N E
   20 5 12 5 16 8 15 14 5

6 P E N I C I L L I N
   16 5 14 9 3 9 12 12 9 14

7 W O R L D W I D E W E B
   23 15 18 12 4 23 9 4 5 23 5 2

5 Read and write. Use the words from Activity 4.

1 This invention is used in cars and airplanes. It made transportation faster. ....
2 This invention helped sailors navigate the seas on long voyages. ....
3 Thanks to this invention, books became cheaper and more popular. ....
4 Inventing this in 3500 B.C. allowed people to transport things on carts. ....
5 It's a medicine that helps treat infections caused by bacteria. ....
6 With this invention, people could talk to each other from far away. ....
7 It's the most modern invention and we have it on our computers. ....

Grammar 1

I/You/She/They **used to** work in the factory.
I/You/He/We **didn't use to** work on the farm.
Did you/she/they **use to** work in the factory?

Yes, I/you/he/they **did**.
No, I/you/she/we **didn't**.

1 Read and circle. Then match.

In the early 19th century …

1 people **use to** / **used to** ride horses in towns.
2 not many girls **use to** / **used to** go to school.
3 city rivers **use to** / **used to** be very dirty.
4 rich people didn't **use to** / **used to** socialize with poor people.
5 poor children **use to** / **used to** work at cotton mills.
6 women didn't **use to** / **used to** play sport.

2 Read and match.

1 Tanya used   a use to like soda.
2 Grandma didn't   b and Sam use to live in the U.S.?
3 Did you   c to go to a village school.
4 Uncle Joe   d read e-books.
5 People didn't use to   e mom use to play the guitar?
6 Did your   f used to ride a motorcycle.

162

3 Write questions. Use the correct form of *used to*.

1 you / live in the same house when you were a baby
....?

2 your parents / go to the same school as you
....?

3 you / play with toy cars when you were young
....?

4 your grandpa / work on a farm
....?

5 your mom / play video games when she was a teenager
....?

4 Answer the questions from Activity 3 for you. Write short answers.

1 ....
2 ....
3 ....
4 ....
5 ....

5 Check (✔) the things that you used to do or have when you were four years old. Then write sentences.

have a pet ☐   live on a farm ☐
go to school ☐   have a smartphone ☐
play with plushies ☐ help with chores ☐

1 ....
2 ....
3 ....
4 ....
5 ....
6 ....

Reading 2

A Day in the Life of Albert Smith

My name is Albert Smith. I'm eight years old. I live in one small room with my father and my brothers and sisters. Our mother died last year and my father is ill and can't work. So, me and my brothers and sisters have to go out to work to earn money. My sisters work on the street as flower sellers and my brothers work in the coal mine. I work in the cotton mill – I have small fingers that are good for making thread. It's hard work, but someone has to do it.

I work 12 hours every day for four shillings per week. Nearly all the workers in the mill are children. We start at six, but at 9 o'clock Timmy, my best friend, still wasn't there. A new child showed up instead. It was his first day, so I had to show him what to do. His name is Charlie and he's six.

Mr Brown, the mill owner, came for inspection at midday. He doesn't speak to the children, he just shouts at us for being lazy. Luckily, he didn't notice that Timmy wasn't there.

After work, I ran to Timmy's house. His sister answered the door.

"Timmy's ill. Did Mr Brown notice he was missing?" she asked.

"No," I said.

"Our plan worked!" she said. "Charlie is our little cousin and we sent him to work in Timmy's place."

"Why didn't he tell me?" I asked.

"He didn't want you to get in trouble with Mr Brown if he started asking questions," she said.

I smiled. Life at the mill is hard, but we stick together.

1 Read *A Day in the Life of Albert Smith* and match.

1 Why can't Albert's father work?
2 Why does Mr. Brown shout at the children?
3 Why did Charlie go to work at the mill?
4 Why didn't Charlie say anything to Albert?

a To pretend to be Timmy.
b He didn't want Albert to get into trouble.
c Because he's sick.
d Because he thinks they're lazy.

2 Discuss with a friend. What problems do you think poor children had in the past?

Vocabulary 2

1 Read, choose, and write. There are two extra words.

| chimney sweep | coal mine | errand | flower girl | housemaid |

1. Very poor people lived in this place in the U.K. in the past. ....
2. This person cleans chimneys on the inside with a long brush. ....
3. It's black dust that comes from wood or coal when we burn it. ....
4. This person cleans a rich person's house. ....
5. It's someone who sells flowers in the street. ....
6. This person kills rats in the street or people's houses. ....
7. It's a person who steals things from people in the street. ....
8. People work there to dig for coal. ....

| pickpocket | ratcatcher | soot | street sweeper | workhouse |

2 Read and complete. There's one extra word.

| chimney sweeps | coal mines | housemaids |
| pickpockets | run errands | soot |

In Victorian London, life for poor children was hard. Small boys often worked as [1] .... and it was dangerous. The black [2] .... got in their lungs and made them sick. Older boys often worked underground in [3] ...., where the conditions were even worse. Children who lived on the streets were used by gangs as [4] .... to steal from the rich. Luckier boys could [5] .... for shop keepers, but they didn't get paid much either.

165

3 Write the jobs in order from the best to the worst in your opinion. Justify your choice.

chimney sweep   flower girl   housemaid   ratcatcher   street sweeper

Best ……………… ……………… ……………… ……………… ……………… **Worst**

……
……
……

Word study: phrasal verbs with *work*

4 Read and match.

1 How much is 20% off? I can't **work**
2 She's a perfectionist. She gets herself **worked**
3 I don't know how to solve this. I'm **working**
4 He has a lot to do. He'll have to **work**
5 My goal is to be a doctor so I'm **working**

a **through** the night!
b **towards** going to university.
c **up** over details.
d **out** how much it costs.
e **on** a solution.

5 Read and write. Use the phrasal verbs from Activity 4.

1 aim for something and work for it
2 solve a problem or plan how to do something
3 work hard to fix a problem
4 make yourself/someone angry or excited
5 work for a long time, often all night

6 Name something …

1 you have to work out.
2 you work towards.
3 you work on.
4 that makes you worked up.

Grammar 2

> This is the machine **that** makes the pollution.
> Doctor Who is the man **who** defeated the Smogator.
> The village is the place **where** the workers lived.

1 Read and circle.

Lady: I'd like the flowers ¹ **that** / **where** are yellow, please.

Flower seller: Here you go. These are the flowers ² **who** / **that** I like best, too.

Lady: Thank you. Are you the girl ³ **where** / **who** always works here?

Flower seller: No. It's my sister ⁴ **who** / **where** usually works here, but she's sick.

Lady: Sorry to hear that. I hope she gets better soon.

2 Read and match.

1. This is the place
2. Mrs. Jones is the woman
3. History is the subject
4. My neighbor is a man who
5. The workhouse is the place where
6. A dictionary is a book that

a. very poor people used to live.
b. that I like best.
c. explains the meanings of words.
d. who's very kind.
e. where my uncle lives.
f. shouts at kids.

3 Complete the sentences. Use *that*, *where*, or *who* and a word from the box.

| book | country | girl | movies | person | village |

1. Mom likes _____ are about the past. *Lincoln* is her favorite.
2. I visited the _____ my grandma was born. It's in the Ireland.
3. Aunt Katy is the _____ you can see in this old picture. She was six!
4. Scotland is the _____ my cousin lives. His house is in Edinburgh.
5. I read a great _____ was about a railway. It's called *The Railway Children*.
6. My dad's the _____ took us to the museum.

4 Answer the questions. Use *that*, *where*, *which*, or *who*.

1 What is the Louvre?

The Louvre is the museum where you can see Mona Lisa.

2 Who is Queen Elizabeth II?

....

3 What is a locomotive?

....

4 Who was Thomas Edison?

....

5 What is a suburb?

....

6 What is the White House?

....

5 Complete the sentences for you and write three more. Use *that*, *where*, or *who*.

1 My bedroom is the place ....
2 My best friend is the person ....
3 The internet is an invention ....
4 ....
5 ....
6 ....

168

Writing

1 Read and circle.

A Day in the City! August 5th, 1906

Today I traveled on a subway train for the first time. I was very excited. I ¹ **used to go / went** on a trip to New York with my father. He works there now. He ² **use to / used to** be a baker, but now he takes the train to the city ³ **where / that** he has a better job.

The train was dirty. I could smell the steam and smoke. The people ⁴ **where / who** were on the train weren't very friendly. But I ⁵ **didn't / didn't use to** care because the train took me to New York for the first time. I saw tall buildings, busy streets, and long bridges. I loved it!

2 Imagine you're a child in the 19th century. Think about how the railway changed your life. Read, circle, and complete.

Date: ....
My life before the railway: ....
....

Feelings and thoughts:

| excited | happy | hate | like | love |
| scared | bored | | | |

....

Changes to my life:

| better | dirty | noisy | travel easily |
| travel quickly | | worse | |

....

3 ✏️ Write your diary entry in your notebook. Use your ideas from Activity 2.

(!) Remember

Check (✓) what your writing has.

a writing strategy:
thoughts and feelings ☐
response to a situation ☐

b vocabulary:
railway words ☐

c grammar:
used to ☐
who/where/that ☐

d correct spelling: ☐

Now I Know

1 Read and circle.

The Rocket

Robert Stephenson was an engineer and inventor **¹ who / where** built *The Rocket*. It was a locomotive **² who / that** he designed in 1829. Newcastle is the city **³ that / where** Stephenson worked and built *The Rocket*. It was fast and it could pull trains with passengers. Before the railway was built, traveling **⁴ used to / use to** take a long time. You could walk or travel in a horse and cart. Did traveling **⁵ use to / used to** be dangerous, too? Yes, it **⁶ used / did**. The countryside didn't **⁷ use to / used to** be safe because of thieves. The railway was the thing **⁸ that / who** changed traveling for everyone.

2 Write the letters in order. Which one was not a job?

1 p e t k p i c k o c k _____
2 s e t t r e s e p w e r e _____
3 y i c h n e m w e p e s _____
4 f w l o e r r i l g _____
5 h e r b u t c _____
6 r a c e r t c h a t _____
7 a h o m i d u s e _____
8 k e b r a _____

A _____ was not a job.

3 Read and complete.

| coal mine | commute | horse and cart |
| marveled | railway | soot | suburbs |

1 Cars travel on roads and trains travel on the _____.
2 I _____ at how quickly the dinner disappeared. We were very hungry!
3 We live in the _____ of Los Angeles and get to the city center by car.
4 People don't usually travel on a _____ today.
5 A _____ is still a dangerous place to work.
6 Many people _____ to work by bus or train.
7 A fireplace is pretty, but the _____ can make the carpet dirty!

4 Complete the sentences.

1 A l_____ is an engine that pulls a train.
2 A c_____ m_____ is a factory where thread and fabric for clothes are made.
3 My parents were tired of living downtown, so we moved to the s_____ .
4 Many people use the s_____ to get to work.
5 The w_____ was a place in U.K. towns where poor people used to live.
6 Boys used to r_____ e_____ for rich people to earn a few shillings.

5 Think about the things you learned in this unit. How is the 19th century different from today?

1 In the past, people used to _____ and _____ .
2 They didn't use to _____ and _____ .
3 The children used to _____ .
4 _____
5 _____

Things I learn

1 Write down your three favorite new words from this unit. Which word was the most difficult?

_____

2 Write two things you found interesting about:

1 the railway   2 jobs people did

_____   _____

_____   _____

3 Would you like to live in the past? Why/Why not?

_____

Pearson Education Limited
KAO TWO
KAO Park
Hockham Way
Harlow, Essex
CM17 9SR
England
and Associated Companies throughout the world.

www.English.com

© Pearson Education Limited 2019

The right of Jennifer Heath to be identified as author of this Work has been asserted by her in accordance with the Copyright, Designs and Patents Act 1988.

All rights reserved; no part of this publication may be reproduced, stored in a retrieval system, or transmitted in any form or by any means, electronic, mechanical, photocopying, recording, or otherwise without the prior written permission of the Publishers.

First published 2019

ISBN: 978-1-292-21966-0

Set in Daytona Pro Semibold 12pt over 17pt

Printed and bound by L.E.G.O. S.p.A. Italy

Image Credit(s):
123RF.com: Denis Ivanov 5, Foodandmore 5, Ulochka 7, Soleg 9, Vincenzo Intiso 9, Shojiro Ishihara 12, Nitr 13, 15, Olegdudko 14, 124, Wavebreak Media Ltd 14, 68, 160, Liza5450 14, Kostrez 14, Martin Rettenberger 14, Tiwaz 14, Antonio Balaguer Soler 15, Cokemomo 17, Goodluz 20, Gábor Kovács 22, Dariia Maksimova 26, Psychoshadowmaker 30, Tonobalaguer 33, Marius Dobilas 34, Byrdyak 34, Witold Kaszkin 35, Dinozzaver 35, Mariusz Jurgielewicz 35, Tatiana Vorona 36, Freezingpic 38, Kian Khoon Tan 44, Vchalup 47, Sondesignx 48, Brian Jackson 48, Sergey Rasulov 48, Bambubam 49, Mykola Velychko 49, Simon Dannhauer 49, Elena Khramova 53, Racorn 63, Ratthaphon Bunmi 67, Stokkete 67, Rostislavsedlacek 67, Dmitriy Shironosov 68, Dimaberkut 68, Atic12 71, Noomhh 77, Siim 81, Matyas Rehak 81, Luckybusiness 86, Satori 87, Alinabuphoto 90, Takashi Honma 90, Viktoriia Kulish 90, Everydayplus 91, Svitlana Varlamova 91, Backgroundstore 91, Aleksandr Prokopenko 91, Kritchanut 91, Cathy Yeulet 92, Viacheslav Iakobchuk 95, Prudencio Alvarez 105, Deklofenak 105, Fabio Formaggio 107, Ostill 109, Lello4d 109, Elenathewise 121, Hartmut Albert 124, Fesus 124, Haveseen 124, Andrey Kiselev 126, Darya Petrenko 129, Soloway 137, Pejo 141, Sonya Etchison 146, Mr. Namart Pieamsuwan 149, Wang Tom 156, Tyler Olson 160, Yobab 168; **Alamy Stock Photo:** Robertharding 19, Fotan 29, Hemis 33, Realimage 48, Dmitry Melnikov 58, North Wind Picture Archives 61, Pictorial Press Ltd 61, Everett Collection Inc 61, Cavan Social 67, SuperStock 85, Gunter Marx 103, Famveld 105, Dmitry Molchanov 105, Blend Images 105, Gregg Vignal 109, Nick Savage 137, Mint Images Limited 150; **BBC Worldwide Learning:** BBC - Co-Branded Products 4, 18, 32, 46, 60, 74, 88, 102, 116, 130, 144, 158; Getty Images: David Aaron Troy 105, VitaliiSmulskyi 111, Zac Macaulay 156; **Image Source:** Zoey 12; **Image State:** John Foxx Collection 124; **Pearson Education Ltd:** Jon Barlow 56; **Shutterstock.com:** Evgeniya68 14, Agnes Kantaruk 14, Upthebanner 20, Constantinos Iliopoulos 20, Beboy 20, Dibrova 20, Jiawangkun 22, Songquan Deng 23, Dennis W Donohue 33, Dudarev Mikhail 35, Andrew F. Kazmierski 35, Luri 35, San Hoyano 39, Idreamphoto 43, Celso Pupo 48, Vladislav Proshkin 48, Walter Bilotta 49, Smereka 49, Rob Hainer 57, UfaBizPhoto 63, MBI 63, 113, Elephotos 67, IvanRiver 67, Creative Jen Designs 67, LightField Studios 68, Igor Bulgarin 68, Johnny Lye 75, Igumnova Irina 77, Ahmad A Atwah 77, 1000 Words 77, Kevin Wells Photography 77, Olga Dar 77, Versta 81, Byelikova Oksana 81, Max Topchii 81, Wead 81, Stanislav Samoylik 90, Ondine C 90, JMiks 91, Kinga 97, Norenko Andrey 103, Digital Storm 109, Luis Molinero 109, Gelpi 120, Africa Studio 123, 155, Jung Hsuan 124, Mike Charles 124, Mangostock 142, Darren Hedges 160, RioPatuca 160, Flamingo Images 160, Studio Dagdagaz 160, Everett Historical 164, 168, Jeff Kinsey 168, Morphart Creation 170, Lux Blue 171.

Cover Images: *Front:* **Getty Images:** Portra

Illustrated by Keri Green (Beehive Illustration) p. 7, 21, 26, 37, 41, 51, 52, 64, 66, 80, 86, 89, 94, 108, 112, 115, 118, 121, 125, 131, 134, 136, 138, 140, 145, 151, 154, 165, 169; The Boy Fitz (NB Illustration) p. 10, 11, 24, 27, 42, 45, 54, 55, 62, 65, 78, 84, 91, 93, 98, 104, 114, 117, 119, 120, 122, 123, 127, 133, 139, 143, 147, 153, 162, 167